CONTENTS

Energy needs pages 4–11

Think about why people need different amounts of food
Find out how we keep our bodies warm
Discover what we need energy for
Calculate how much energy we use climbing stairs
Find out how to keep at the right weight
Learn about anorexia
Investigate your body temperature
Give advice on how to keep warm in winter

A balanced diet pages 12–19

Look at healthy and unhealthy meals
Investigate malnutrition around the world
Find out what to eat to stay healthy
Discover what vitamins and minerals are for
See how vitamin C could save an explorer's life
Survey the additives in packaged food
Research the cost of different types of food
Explain how to cook food without breaking down vitamins
Recommend a diet for a body builder
See whether your friends are eating a healthy diet

Getting food into the body pages 20–27

Think about how food changes as it goes through the body
Consider what a drip-feed is for
Learn how food gets to all parts of your body
Find out more about digestion
Explain how some digestive illnesses can be treated
Interpret the results of some experiments on digestion

Energy from food pages 28–35

Research the supplies an astronaut needs in a spacesuit
Learn about the structure of the lungs
Study experiments showing how we get energy from food
See how respiration can be shown as a chemical equation
Discover how oxygen travels from the lungs to the cells
Write a report on smoking and make a poster

Working hard and keeping fit pages 36–43

Discover how your body adjusts to exercise
See whether you are living a healthy life
Learn how you keep cool
Discover how to measure fitness
Give advice to get someone fit

Data pages pages 44–45

Tables of food values

Extension activities pages 46–47

Analyse diets and plan healthy meals

Index page 48

ENERGY FOR LIVING

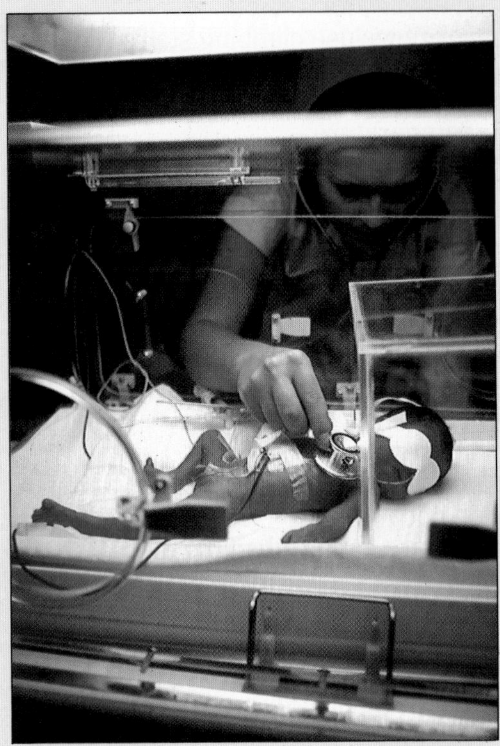

A *All the people shown above need energy. Discuss each picture and decide what each person is using most energy for. Summarise your findings in a table.*

B *Think about your family and friends. Make a list of them in order of how much food they eat. Try to guess why the ones at the top of your list need most energy and why the ones at the bottom need the least. Put your guesses next to each person's name.*

OXFORD

WILLIAM MERRICK
JOAN O'SULLIVAN

THE HUMAN BODY

Oxford University Press, Walton Street, Oxford OX2 6DP

Oxford New York Toronto
Delhi Bombay Calcutta Madras Karachi
Petaling Jaya Singapore Hong Kong Tokyo
Nairobi Dar es Salaam Cape Town
Melbourne Auckland

and associated companies in
Berlin Ibadan

Oxford is a trade mark of Oxford University Press

ISBN 0 19 914319 6

Typeset in Century Old Style & Helvetica Light Italic
Pentacor PLC, High Wycombe, Bucks
Printed in Hong Kong

First published 1990

WRITING TEAM

David Appleby, Biddenham Upper School, Bedford
Alan Jarvis, Inspector, Bedfordshire LEA
William Merrick, Challney High School, Luton
Joan O'Sullivan, Putteridge High School, Luton
Pam Slade, Science Advisor, Redbridge

To my wife Judith and my daughters Angela and Lucy. (WM)

I wish to thank my husband Eugene for all his help in producing this book. (JO'S)

We wish to thank Oxford University Press for their confidence in us and for their valuable contributions and help at all stages of production.

ACKNOWLEDGEMENTS

Allsport: pp 36, 38, 39; John Cleare/Mountain Camera: p4; Bruce Coleman: p13; Colorsport: pp 4 (bottom), 18, 39; Corning Ltd: p 18 (bottom right); Popperfoto: p 16 (centre, bottom); Rex Features: p 9 (top, centre, bottom); Science Photo Library: pp 4 (left), 16 (top), 21, SPL/E. Grave 23 (left), SPL/Leroy (right), SPL/Novosti 28, 40; Zefa Photographic Library: p5.

Additional photography by Marilyn O'Brien. Illustrations by Oena Armstrong, Susannah English, Gordon Hendry, Rachel Lockwood, Julie Tolliday and Galina Zolfaghari. Cover illustration by Paul Hunt.

The authors wish to thank: The Health Education Council.

HOT AND COLD

The body uses about 80% of the energy obtained from food simply to maintain a body temperature of 37°C. A thermal image can show the parts of the body that lose heat the fastest. The warmest parts of the body are coloured red and the coldest parts blue.

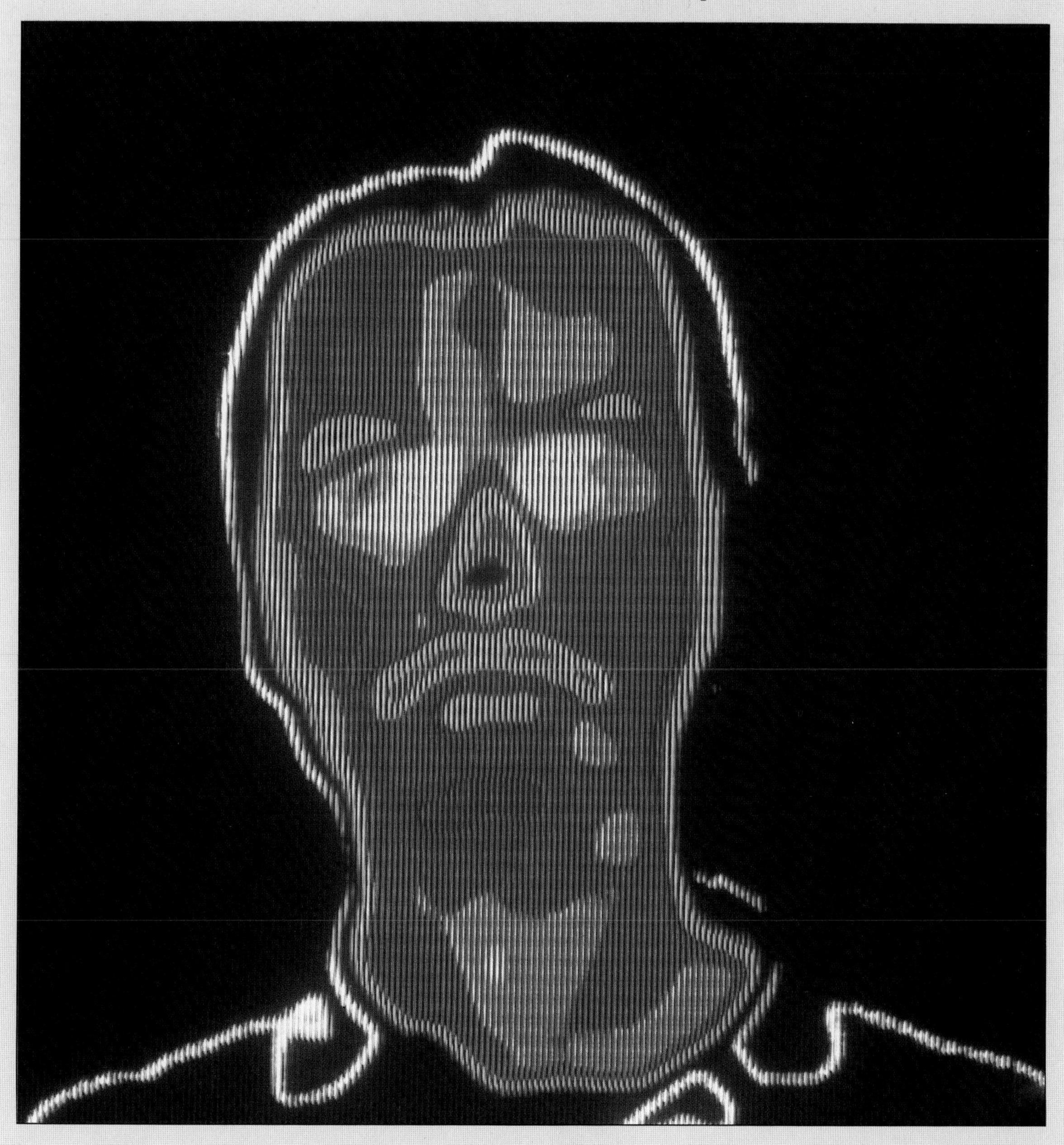

A *Which parts of your body lose heat the fastest? Why do you think they are the hardest to keep warm? Which important organs are in the warmest parts of the body?*

B *Find out what problems are caused if the main part of the body gets too cold*

C *Make a list of all the things you do to keep warm in cold weather. Don't forget to think about what you eat.*

FACTFILE

ENERGY NEEDS

MEASURING ENERGY

We measure energy in units called **joules**. *One joule is a very small amount of energy. It is the amount needed to lift a weight of one newton through one metre.*

apple (weight 1 newton)

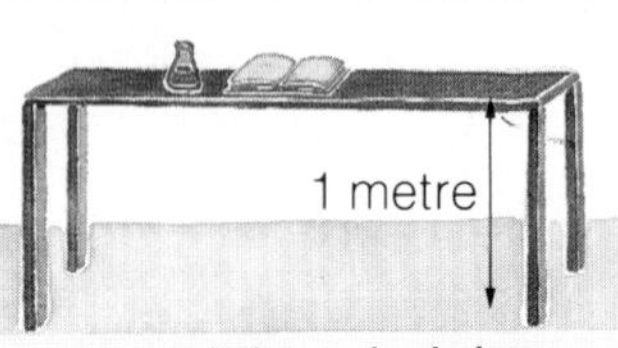

energy used = **weight × height**
= *1N × 1m*
= **1 joule**

We use millions of joules every day and so it is convenient to measure the energy in food in kilojoules (kJ). There are 1000 joules in 1 kilojoule.

man (weight 850 newtons)

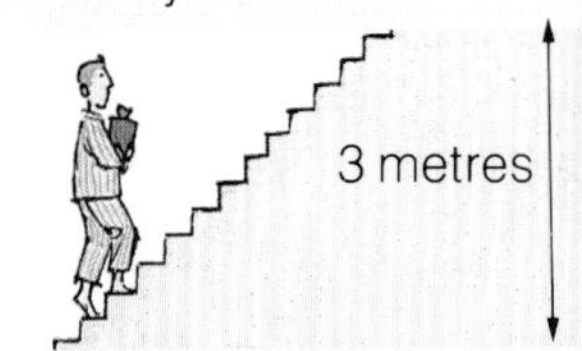

energy used = **weight × height**
= *850N × 3m*
= **2550 joules**
= **2.55 kilojoules**

WE ALL NEED ENERGY

The food we eat is our fuel. It gives us the energy we need. A car could not move without using the energy stored in petrol. In the same way we could not move unless we used the energy stored in food.

WE NEED ENERGY TO MOVE, TO KEEP WARM AND TO GROW

Energy to move
All our muscles use energy. This includes the heart and the muscles used for breathing.

Energy for warmth
Our bodies are at 37°C. The temperature outside may be only 0°C. Energy from food stops us cooling down.

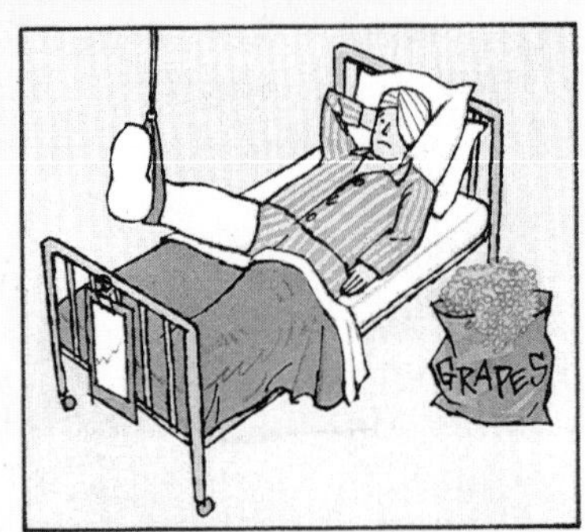

Energy to grow
Growing is hard work and uses a lot of energy. Repairing injuries to the body also uses a lot of energy.

HOW MUCH ENERGY DO WE NEED?

These charts show how many kilojoules of energy per day are needed by various types of people.

Different people need different amounts of energy.

- *People who have strenuous jobs use more energy and so need more food.*
- *Young people who are growing must eat more food than those who are not.*
- *People working outside require more energy for warmth.*
- *Women who are pregnant or breastfeeding need more energy.*
- *Males usually need more energy than females.*

We don't usually need to look at a chart to see how much food we should eat! Our appetite naturally makes us eat the right amount.

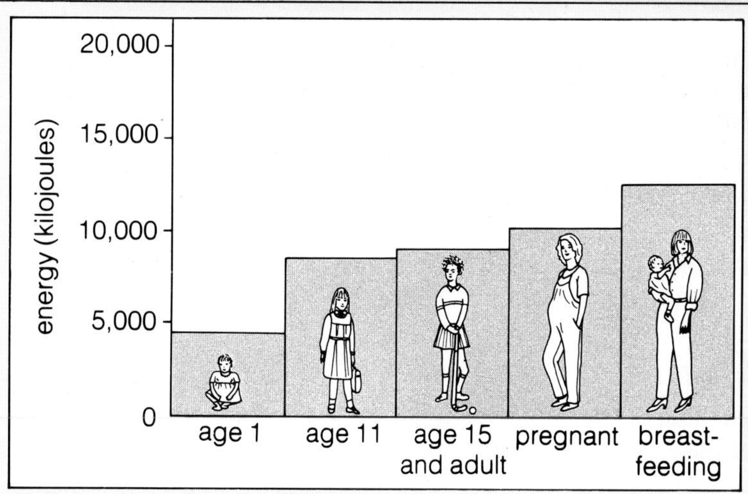

Daily energy requirements (females)

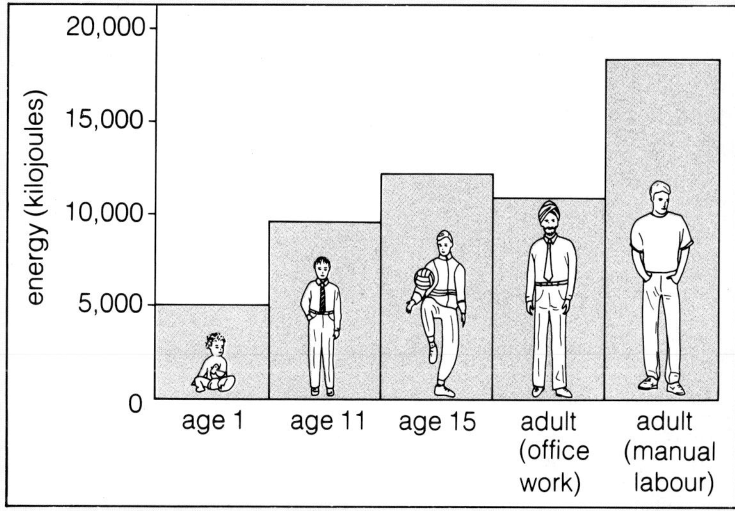

Daily energy requirements (males)

GETTING FAT

Sometimes we eat too much. Our bodies will turn the extra energy into fat in order to store it for a time when we do not eat enough.

People who put on too much weight have to make sure that the energy they take in as food is not more than the amount of energy they use up.

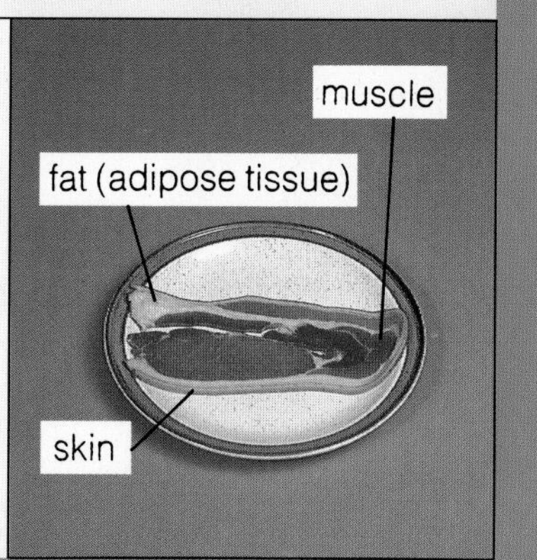

COLD KILLS

Normal body temperature is 37°C. If the core temperature of the body drops below 35°C **hypothermia** *results. This can kill. People lost on mountains or at sea are at risk, and so are old people on poor diets.*

About 80% of the energy in our food is used to keep us warm.

EATING THE RIGHT AMOUNT

The amount of food we need to eat changes from time to time. We need to eat more in the winter or if we are doing a lot of sport or heavy work. Some people find it hard to match their energy intake with their energy use.

They may find themselves feeling tired and losing weight if they eat too little, or putting on weight if they eat more than they need. Charts like the one below show us what our healthiest weight should be.

Weight and height

The chart is for adult women. Similar charts can be drawn for men. Men have a different build to women, and can be a little heavier. A man can weigh about 4.5 kilograms (10 pounds) more than a woman of the same height. Schoolchildren's weight can vary a lot as they grow, so these charts are not very reliable for them. You can see from the chart that there is quite a range of healthy weights. A woman who is 1.63m tall (5 feet 4 inches) can safely weigh between 48 and 64 kilos (7½ to 10 stones).

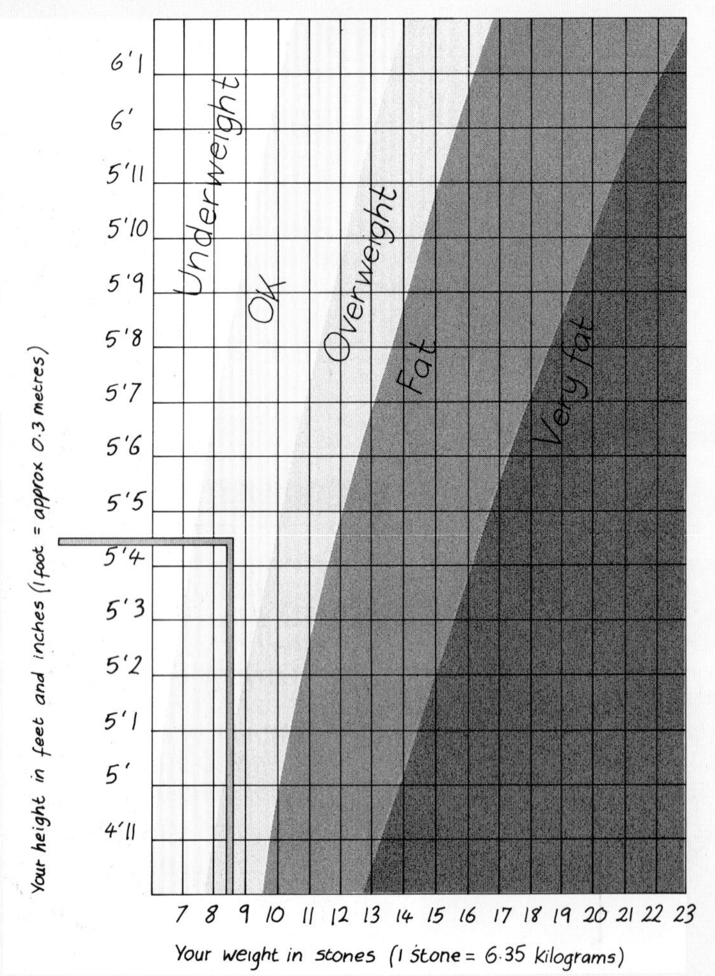

A *Do you think your appetite adjusts your eating habits to fit in with what you have been doing? Test this by making a note of what you eat on the following days:*

- *a day when you have games at school;*
- *a winter day when you spend a lot of time outside;*
- *a day you go swimming;*
- *a warm day spent relaxing at home.*

B *Summarise your findings by completing the sentences below.*

I find I eat more when . . . .
I find I eat less when . . . .

Looking good

Many people are very concerned about their weight. Some people think they are too fat, while others are worried that they look too thin.

Unfortunately our ideas on the *right* weight are often more to do with fashion than with health – and fashions change! Look at the pictures on the right.

Fifties' actress, Diana Dors

Sixties' model, Twiggy

David Bowie as Ziggy Stardust

Anorexia nervosa – the slimmer's disease

What is anorexia? People with anorexia refuse to eat. They are so afraid of putting on weight that they can control their feelings of hunger. It often begins as *slimming* but carries on until the victim is dangerously weak and ill. Girl sufferers stop having their periods. The disease can last several years and although most sufferers recover some do die.

Who gets anorexia? Most victims are girls between the ages of 15 and 25, although boys may also get it. About 1% of girls are affected. Often they are worried about something in their lives for example doing well at school, or coping as a grown up.

What is the treatment? In serious cases treatment in hospital is needed. Patients are looked after, encouraged to eat, and given help with their worries.

Why do people become anorexic?

These are quotes from people who have recovered.

'When I was young other kids made fun of me because of my weight.'

'I was worried about a lot of things. I thought that if I could look perfect then the rest of my life would be perfect.'

'I don't know where it went past the safe point. I got down to seven stones. That's thin, but I didn't see that in the mirror. I still thought I looked fat.'

'I was hungry, but I thought I would hate myself for eating. It was a battle between me and food.'

'My friend is slim and all the boys like her. I just wanted to be popular too.'

Remember that the kind of person we are is really more important than what we look like. Being a **healthy** weight is more important than being a **fashionable** weight.

Questions and Activities

A Use the bar charts on page 7 to make a table showing how much food energy the different people need each day. Put them in order, starting with the one who needs the least. Put males and females together on the same chart.

person	energy needed per day (kJ)
girl, age 1	4,500

B Look back to the activity on page 4 in which you had to list your family and friends in order of how much food they ate.

You tried to guess why each person ate what they did. Improve those explanations now you have studied this unit.

C Some people seem to eat a lot but never get fat. Other people are less lucky. They eat quite small amounts and still put on too much weight. Explain why this happens.

D What advice would you give to someone who needs to lose weight?

E How much energy do you use every day just climbing the stairs at home? You will need to know:

a) your weight in newtons (this is your mass in kilograms multiplied by 10);
b) the height of your stairs in metres;
c) the number of times you climb the stairs each day.

The way to work this out is shown in the **factfile**.

F A channel swimmer has become exhausted and has hypothermia. Her temperature has dropped to 35°C. Calculate how much energy is needed to warm her up to 37°C.

Assume that a person's body is mostly water. 4.2 kilojoules are needed to warm up 1 kilogram of water by 1°C. The swimmer has a mass of 70 kilograms.

G Unless something is wrong our body temperature is always kept very near to 37°C.

Check this statement. Use clinical thermometers to make a survey of the body temperature of everyone in your class. Your teacher will show you the correct way to do this. Try to get temperatures under different conditions:

a) when feeling hot after exercise;

b) after being outside in the cold;

c) when sitting normally in the classroom.

- Record the temperature of the room at the same time. How much warmer than the room are you?
- Write an explanation of the process going on inside you that keeps you warm.

A right to be warm

For many people cold weather can be the cause of much discomfort and misery. For some it may seriously affect their health.

There are people who may be able to help or advise with things that can be done to keep warmer in winter.

SOME POINTS TO REMEMBER

Many people do not claim all that they may be ENTITLED to (eg Rate Rebate, Supplementary Pension). Even a little extra money can make all the difference towards heating costs. Getting advice on benefits can help to make sure you're getting all that is yours BY RIGHT.

Dept. of Health and Social Security, Social Services, Citizens Advice Bureau, Age Concern.

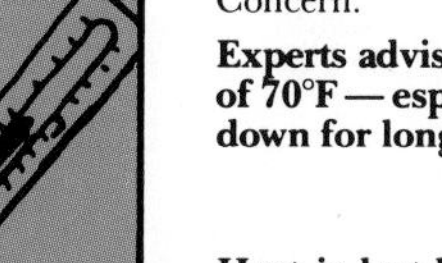

Experts advise a living room temperature of 70°F — especially if someone is sitting down for long periods of time.

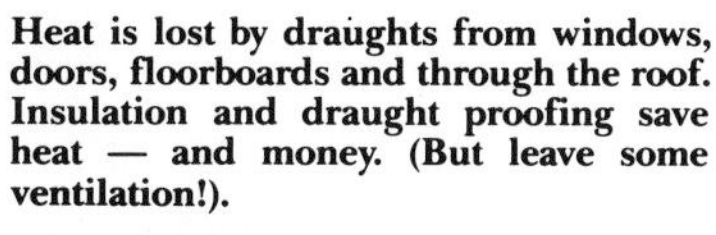

Heat is lost by draughts from windows, doors, floorboards and through the roof. Insulation and draught proofing save heat — and money. (But leave some ventilation!).

D.H.S.S., Social Security, Dept. of Environmental Health, C.A.B., Age Concern.

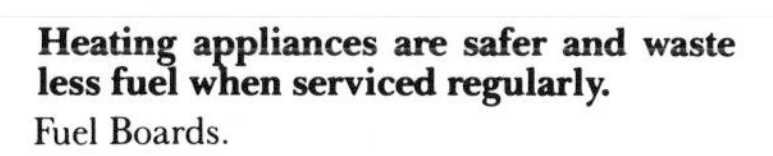

Heating appliances are safer and waste less fuel when serviced regularly.

Fuel Boards.

Nourishing and regular meals are even more important in winter. Food fuels the body and helps to fight the cold.

An emergency food store cupboard is a good idea in case bad weather or illness prevents shopping trips.

Meals on Wheels Services and Luncheon Clubs run in many areas — it's worth asking about them.

Social Services, C.A.B., Age Concern.

A few layers of light-weight clothes will trap heat from the body and so are better than heavy clothes for keeping warm.

A thermal underblanket, a covered hot-water bottle OR an electric overblanket if used carefully, can make a big difference to being warm in bed. Even socks, gloves and a hat can help to keep in body heat.

A bed moved into the living room (put next to the inside wall) means one less room to keep warm.

Turn over to see who can help.

In England about 40,000 more people die in the winter months than in the summer. Most of the extra deaths are among old people. Various illnesses are made worse in cold weather. These include bronchitis, heart disease and strokes.

About 500 of the winter deaths are caused by **hypothermia** – the body becomes too cold to survive.

People on low incomes (like many pensioners) often have to save money on food, warm clothes and fuel bills. This leaflet has been produced to advise old people on ways of surviving the winter.

Write an introduction to go with the leaflet. Remember you are writing for people who may not know a lot of science.

You have to explain:

- what hypothermia is;
- why it is a special risk for old people;
- how a good diet can help.

A HEALTHY APPETITE

These two meals would both give you the energy you need. In other ways they are very different.

A *Discuss the two meals with your class. Think about all of the things you have heard about healthy eating.*

Make a list of changes that could be made to the unhealthy meal to improve it.

B *Do you choose healthy meals? Think back to the last time you chose a meal for yourself. Perhaps it was in the school canteen or when you went out to eat in a restaurant.*

Write down what you had to eat. Was it a healthy meal or was it an unbalanced one?

FEED THE WORLD

A poor diet causes health problems all over the world. Two thirds of the world live in poverty and do not get enough to eat. In richer countries people can make themselves ill by eating too much of the wrong food.

A *Colour in a map of the world to show which countries have enough food and which ones have too little. Your school atlas may have the information.*

B *Find out about what is being done to provide food for starving people. Make a list of organisations trying to help.*

FACTFILE

A BALANCED DIET

FOOD TYPES

Protein
We need this to grow and mend our bodies. Muscles are made of protein.

Water
Our bodies are 65% water. It is very important in all body processes and is also used to carry waste out of the body.

Carbohydrate
Starches and sugars give us the energy we need. If we miss these out fat or muscle will be used instead.

Minerals
These are simple chemicals found naturally in food.

Fats and oils
These supply more energy than other foods. We store energy as fat.

Vitamins
We need these to stay healthy. There are many vitamins, and each one has a special job to do in the body.

Each type of food does a different job. We must eat some of each. A varied diet with the right amount of each type is called a **balanced diet.**

Each of the vitamins and minerals has its own function. We only need tiny amounts, but if we miss them out completely we may suffer **deficiency diseases**. *These are caused because some vital body function is not being done properly.*

FIBRE

Fibre is the part of our food which we do not digest. It passes right through our gut and leaves the body as solid waste (faeces) when we go to the toilet. The right amount of fibre in our diet keeps our intestines healthy and working properly. It makes the food in our gut soft and moist so it can move along quickly and easily. Without fibre we become constipated. This can eventually damage the gut. Lack of fibre may cause piles, appendicitis and even cancer. Brown bread, brown rice and crunchy vegetables contain a lot of fibre.

WE MUST EAT DIFFERENT TYPES OF FOOD

No food is perfect on its own. The foods we buy contain differing amounts of protein, carbohydrate, fat and fibre. We can only get the right amount of each if we eat a wide variety of foods. The different parts of this sandwich add up to a healthy snack.

Bread
carbohydrate 48%
fat 2%
water 39%
fibre 3%
protein 8%

Margarine
fat 82%
water 18%

Chicken
fat 4%
water 69%
protein 27%

Lettuce
carbohydrate 1%
water 96%
fibre 2%
protein 1%

DEFICIENCY DISEASES

Vitamins *are complicated chemicals found only in living things. They are easily destroyed by heat.*

vitamin	good sources	function	deficiency disease
A	milk, liver, greens, carrots	formation of light sensitive chemical in eye	**night blindness**
B	yeast, meat, liver	helps with many chemical reactions e.g. respiration	**beri-beri**, a disease affecting nerves and muscles
C	fruit and vegetables, citrus fruits	formation of *collagen* – connective tissue	**scurvy** leads to poor healing and growth
D	fish oils, eggs, milk, also made in skin by sunlight (ultraviolet)	helps body use calcium to form strong bones	**rickets** causes weak bones and bent limbs

Minerals *are much simpler. They are found in foods or in simple chemicals such as salt.*

mineral	good sources	function	deficiency disease
calcium	milk, cheese, bread, greens	calcium phosphate gives bone its strength	weak bones and teeth
iodine	fish, table salt which has iodine added	used in the thyroid gland to make a hormone called thyroxine	**cretinism**, a disease causing poor growth and mental handicap in children **slow metabolism** (body chemistry) in adults
iron	liver, eggs, greens	used in red blood cells to make haemoglobin	**anaemia**, a disease in which blood carries less oxygen, causing weakness and tiredness

VITAMIN C

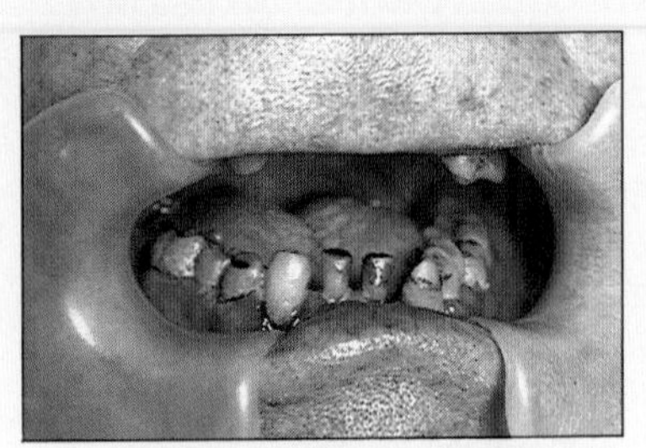

The mouth of a scurvy victim

Strong threads of **collagen** are found in all parts of the body. Without vitamin C we cannot make collagen. Collagen holds teeth in place and joins muscles to bones. The walls of tiny blood vessels (capillaries) are strengthened by it. Scars which heal wounds are made of it. Victims of scurvy are weak and tired, and suffer from pulled muscles.

The history of vitamin C

Scurvy has been known for thousands of years. People noticed that the symptoms appeared at the end of winter but they had no idea of the causes of the disease.

The long sea journeys of the 1400's gave a clue. When Vasco da Gama sailed from Europe to India, half of his men died of scurvy. The poor diet on ships began to be suspected as a cause.

In 1753 James Lind, a doctor in the Royal Navy, carried out an early type of **fair test**. He gave sailors with scurvy all types of extra things to eat. Some were given cider to drink, some sea water, some vinegar, and some were even given drops of sulphuric acid! The lucky ones were given **oranges and lemons** to eat and were cured.

In 1775 Captain Cook kept his men healthy by giving them **onions** and **pickled cabbage**. The navy started giving all sailors a ration of **lime juice**.

In 1932 a doctor in Hungary extracted ascorbic acid (the chemical name for vitamin C) from **green peppers**.

As with all vitamins only tiny amounts of vitamin C are needed. 0.1g a day is more than enough to keep you healthy.

In 1912 a British expedition, lead by Captain Scott, attempted to reach the South Pole on foot, pulling their own sledges without using dogs. They reached the Pole, but all died on the way back to base camp. They had only preserved food in tins. They had meat, biscuits, sugar, fat and some raisins. None of the foods contained vitamin C.

Scotts' party set out

we shall stick it out
to the end but we
are getting weaker of
course and the end
cannot be far.
It seems a pity but
I do not think I can
write more –
R Scott
Last Entry
For Gods sake look
after our people

The last words in Captain Scotts' journal

A *List the signs of scurvy mentioned in the text above.*

B *Suggest ways in which vitamin C could have been taken on the journey.*

C *Find out how modern explorers solve the problem.*

FOOD ADDITIVES

Many foods have substances added to them. An additive is anything which is not normally part of that food. They are added to food for various reasons. Flavours and colours are put in to make the food more attractive. Preservatives prevent food from going bad.

Some additives are chemicals but others are natural products used in an unusual way. For example carotene is a yellow/orange colour extracted from carrots. It is added to margarine to make it look yellow.

By law food has to be labelled to show the additives. The name of the additive may appear on the packaging, or a code (the E number) may be used.

INGREDIENTS: PORK, WATER, RUSK, STARCH, TURKEY, SALT, SPICES, SOYA PROTEIN CONCENTRATE, SODIUM POLYPHOSPHATE, HERBS, DEXTROSE, FLAVOUR ENHANCER (MONOSODIUM GLUTAMATE), ANTIOXIDANT (E301, E304, E307), SUGAR, PRESERVATIVE (E223), FLAVOURING, COLOUR (E128).

Packaged pork sausages

Are additives safe?

It is illegal to put anything in food which injures health. Everything has to be tested to show it is safe. The quote below is from the leaflet 'Food additives' issued by MAFF, the Ministry of Agriculture Fisheries and Food.

By 'safe', we mean safe for everyone except those people who have adverse reactions to particular additives – between three and 15 people in 10,000. This is far less than the number of people who have adverse reactions to foods such as strawberries or shellfish.

545	Ammonium polyphosphates
E160(b)	Annatto
E163	Anthocyanins
E300	L-Ascorbic acid
E304	Ascorbyl palmitate
E333	*mono*Calcium citrate
E333	*di*Calcium citrate
E333	*tri*Calcium citrate
E238	Calcium formate

Some of the E numbers

Should we avoid additives?

If certain foods make you feel ill you may be allergic to one of the additives. You will need to study the labels to try to find out which one might be causing the problem. It is possible to avoid most additives. Fresh foods do not normally contain them.

A difficult decision

E250 and *E251* are sodium nitrate and sodium nitrite. Some evidence suggests that eating large amounts of them may be a cancer risk. They are added to cured meat to stop a germ growing which causes a deadly form of food poisoning called **botulism**.

A *Look at the labels on the food packets that you have at home. Write down all of the additives you can find.*

B *Sort them into lists of preservatives, colours and flavours. Which one could have been left out without making the food unsafe?*

C *What other foods could you have eaten instead to avoid the additives?*

Questions and Activities

A What kind of diet would you recommend for an athlete who is training to build up her muscles? Give a list of foods you would recommend, and explain why you have chosen them.

B Use the **factfile** to make a summary chart of the different parts of a healthy balanced diet.

food type	found in	needed for
protein carbohydrate fat water vitamins minerals fibre		

C Different kinds of food cost different amounts. Visit the shops and find the cost of foods high in protein, carbohydrate and fat. Find three examples of each type. To make it fair find the cost of 100 grams of each food.

food type	example	cost for 100g
protein	1. fish 2. 3.	
carbohydrate	1. sugar 2. 3.	
fats and oils	1. margarine 2. 3.	

- If someone tried to save money by eating only the cheapest foods, what food type might they be missing out?
- What health problems would they have if they did this for too long?

D Vitamins soon break down once a food is cut up. They are also easily spoiled if they are heated for a long time. If the foods are cooked in a lot of water the vitamins are washed out.

Write an article for a recipe book explaining the best way to cook cauliflower so as to keep most of its vitamins.

Keep your balance

protein	examples	numbers of pupils
healthy	high protein, low fat (e.g. fish, eggs)	
unhealthy	low protein, high fat (e.g. sausages, burgers)	

vitamins	examples	numbers of pupils
healthy	fresh salads, fruit, vegetables (e.g. lettuce, oranges)	
unhealthy	overcooked vegetables or no vegetables	

fibre	examples	numbers of pupils
healthy	vegetables, salad, fruit, baked beans, brown bread, jacket potatoes	
unhealthy	none of the above, white bread or rice	

carbohydrate	examples	numbers of pupils
healthy	high carbohydrate (e.g. mashed or boiled potato, rice, pasta)	
unhealthy	too greasy	

- Do the pupils in your school eat a healthy diet? Carry out a survey in the school canteen. To get a fair picture you will need to look at about twenty different people.
- Count the numbers of people choosing the foods in the charts above.
- Display your results as bar charts or pie charts. You could make them into posters for your classroom. Perhaps you could display them in the canteen.
- Make up a list of advice for people choosing their meals in the canteen. For example your first point could be *always have some vegetables*.

WE ALL NEED FOOD

It takes many hours for the food we have eaten to pass through the **alimentary canal** (gut) before some of it leaves as waste from the anus. Certain materials may take several days to pass through the body.

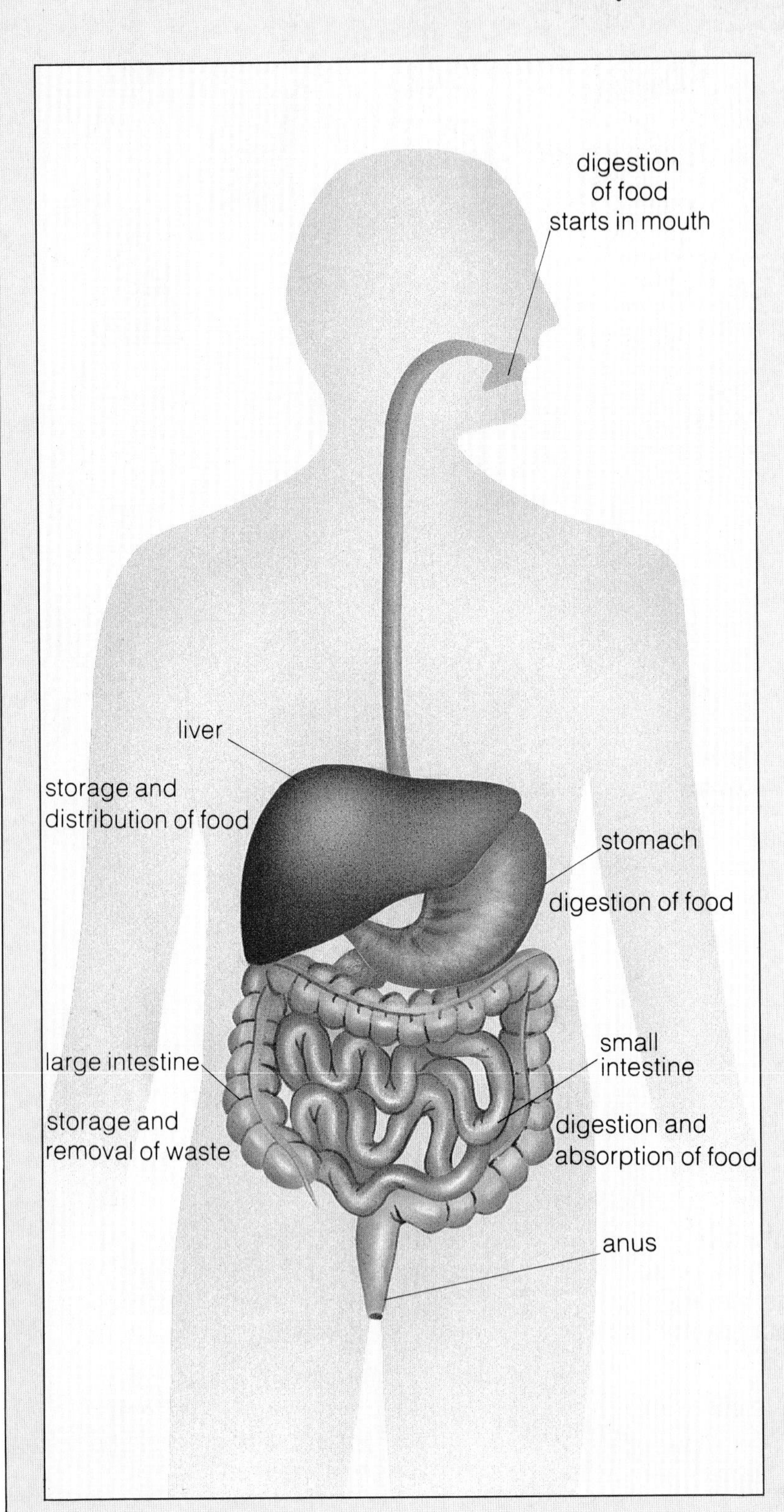

A *The gut is not just a large cavity. In fact it is seven metres long from beginning to end! Why do you think it needs to be so long?*

B *The food is changed as it passes through the gut.*

- *List the differences between what goes in as food and what comes out as waste.*
- *What happens to the food as it passes through the gut?*

DRIP FEED

Maria has been taken to hospital after a road accident. She has been unconscious for several days. The doctor has fitted a tube into a blood vessel in her arm. A food solution is being dripped into her blood.

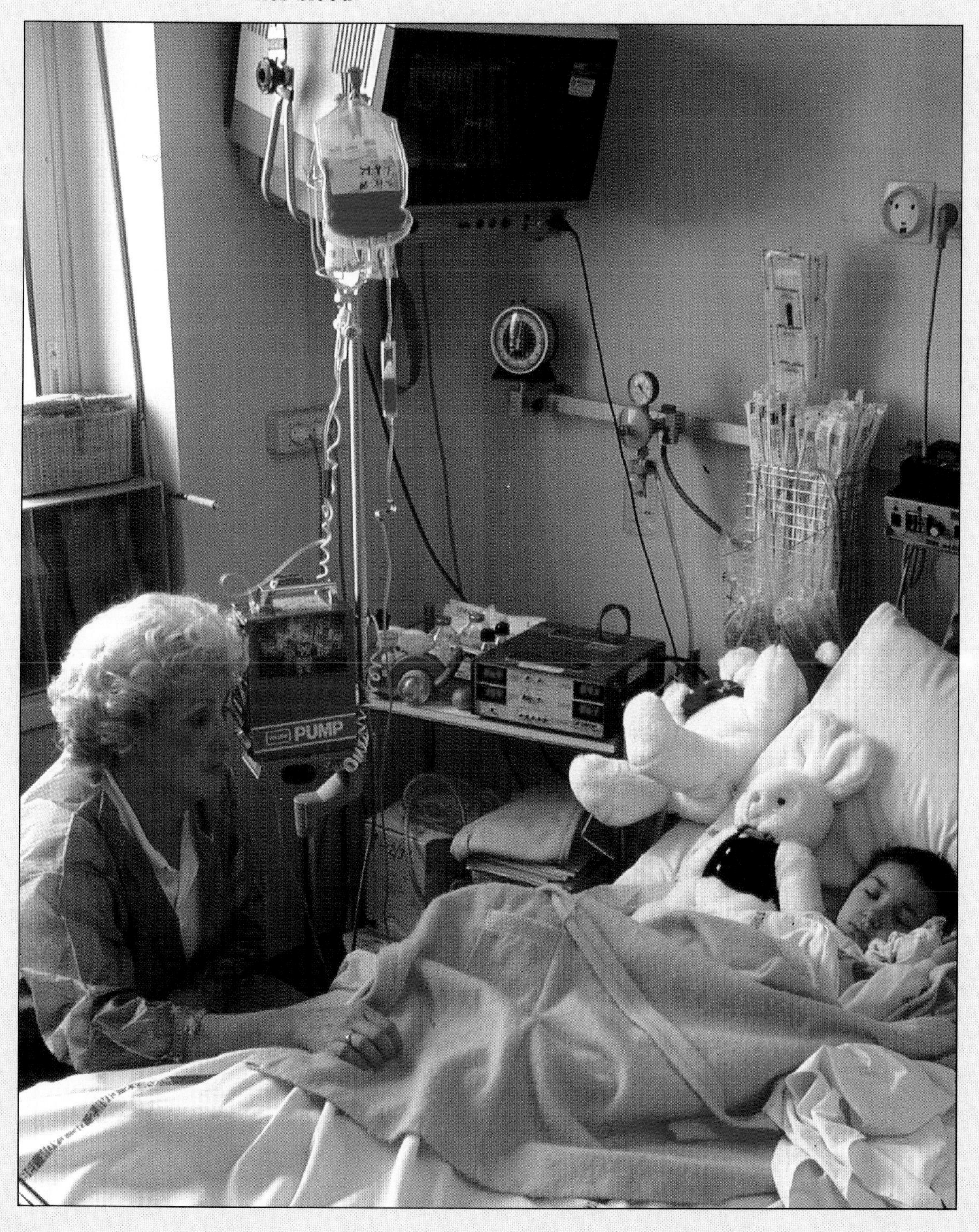

A *If she is not moving, why does she still need food?*

B *Why is the food put into her blood rather than given to her as solid food?*

FACTFILE

GETTING FOOD INTO THE BODY

SOLUBLE FOOD

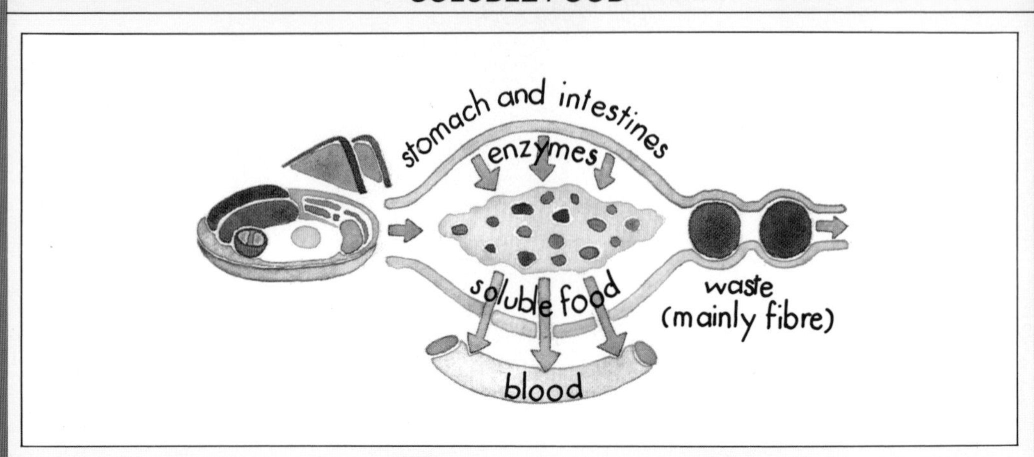

Blood carries food to all parts of our body. Food cannot travel through the body as sausage, egg, bacon and tomato because the blood can only carry soluble food. The food we eat is made up of **small, soluble molecules**, *such as sugars and vitamins and* **large molecules which are insoluble**. *Digestion occurs in the gut where large molecules are broken down into smaller, soluble ones which can then be carried in the blood.*

The body makes **enzymes** *which speed up the digestion of food. Enzymes are designed to work best at body temperature.*

Enzymes enable the large molecules to be broken up into smaller molecules. When the food reaches the small intestine it is changed into these small molecules which can pass through the wall of the small intestine and into the blood.

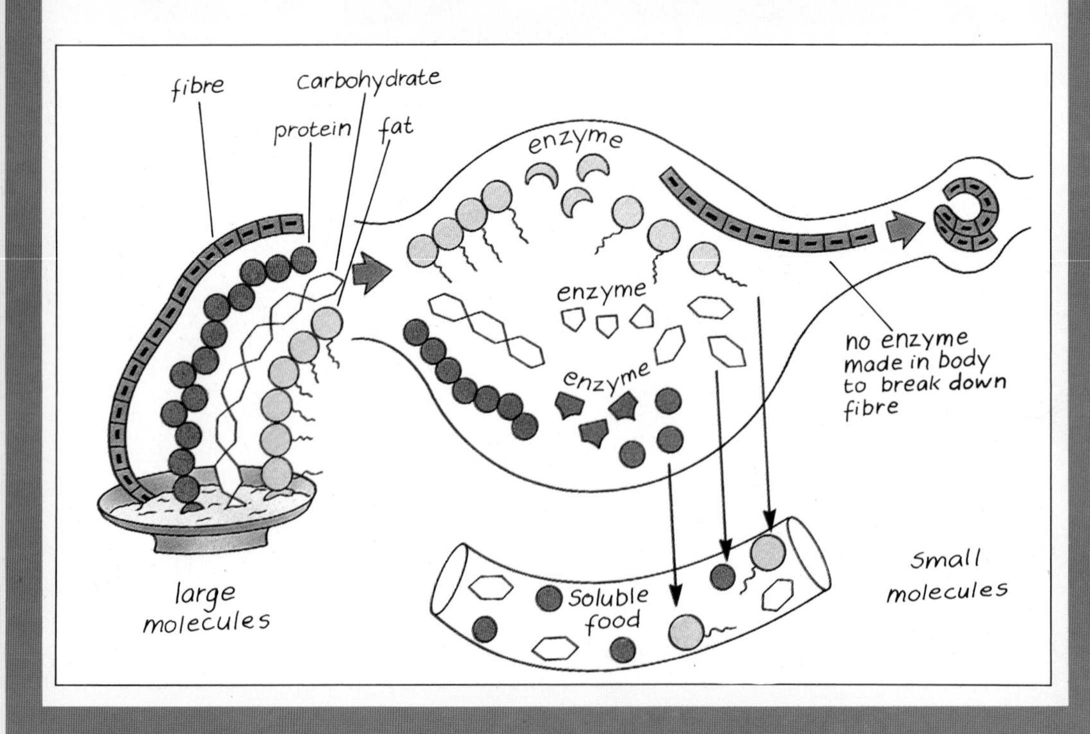

A MODEL GUT

Visking tubing *is a type of plastic which behaves in a similar way to the small intestine. It can be used to make a model gut. A suspension of starch in water is placed into one tube. Starch solution with an enzyme called* **amylase** *is placed in a second tube. Both tubes are then left in water. After 15 minutes the water surrounding each tube is tested for the presence of starch and sugars.*

The enzyme **amylase** *has broken down the starch into soluble sugars which have passed through the visking tubing. The same thing happens with the soluble food in the small intestine. It can pass through the wall of the intestine into the blood stream.*

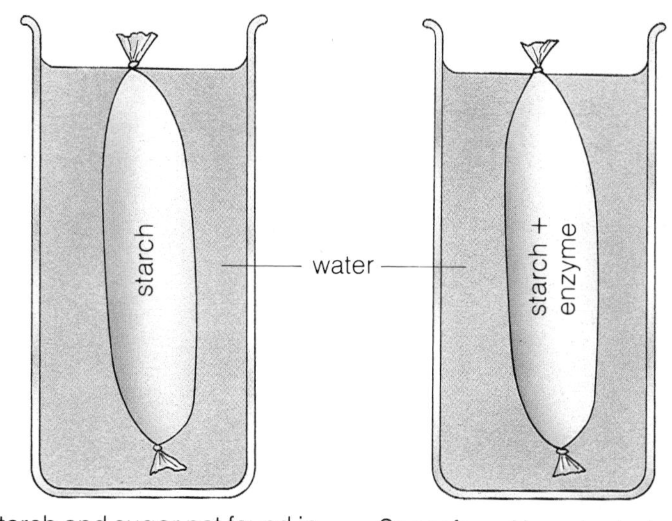

Starch and sugar not found in water

Sugar found in water but no starch detected

ABSORPTION OF SOLUBLE FOOD

The intestine is about seven metres long. Inside it is covered with finger-like projections called **villi**. *These increase the surface area of the gut so that all of the soluble food can be absorbed. The villi contain blood vessels which carry the soluble food away from the intestine.*

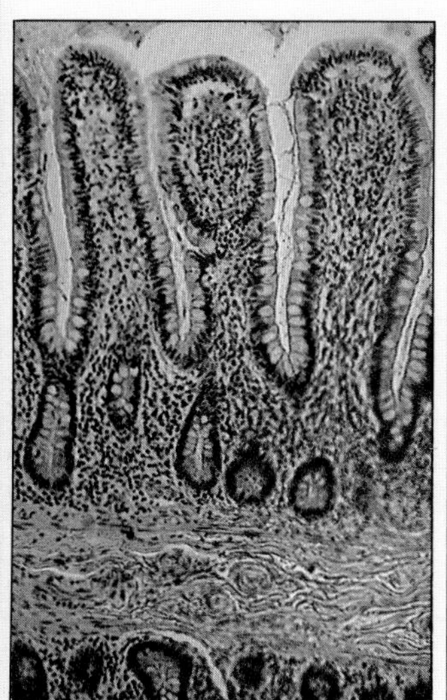

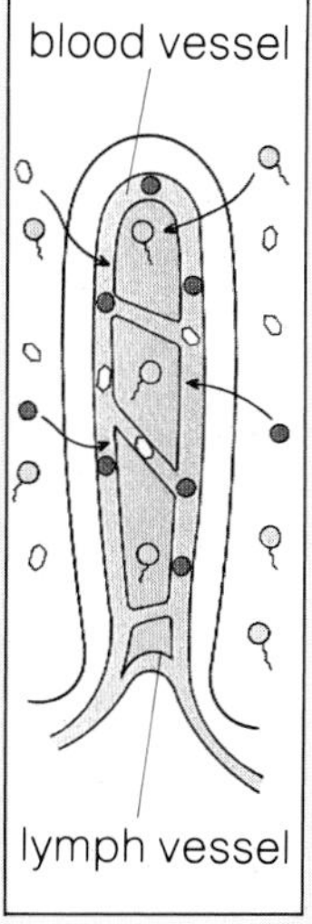

TRANSPORT OF FOOD

Plasma *is the liquid part of the blood. It carries the soluble food first to the liver and then to all parts of the body.*

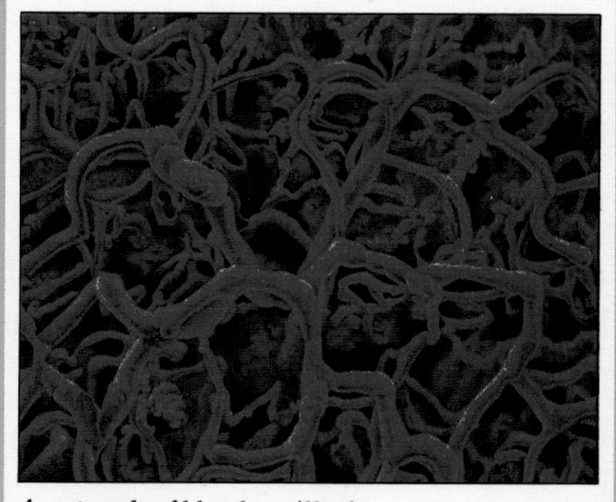

A network of blood capillaries

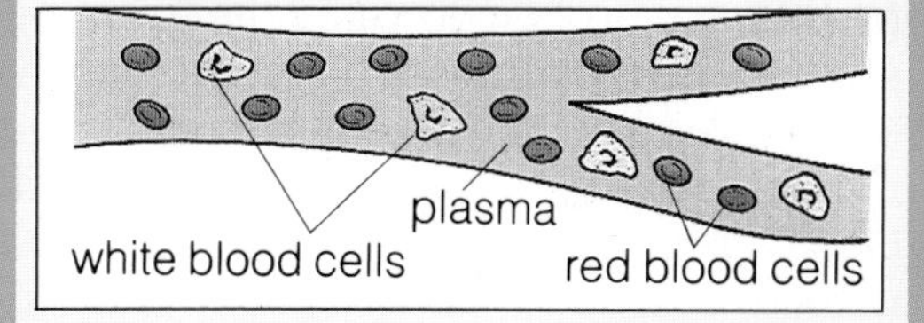

EATING AND DIGESTION

What makes you feel hungry? Low levels of sugars in cells and an empty stomach cause messages to be sent to the brain to make you feel hungry. A full stomach sends messages to the brain which tell you that you are satisfied and no longer hungry.

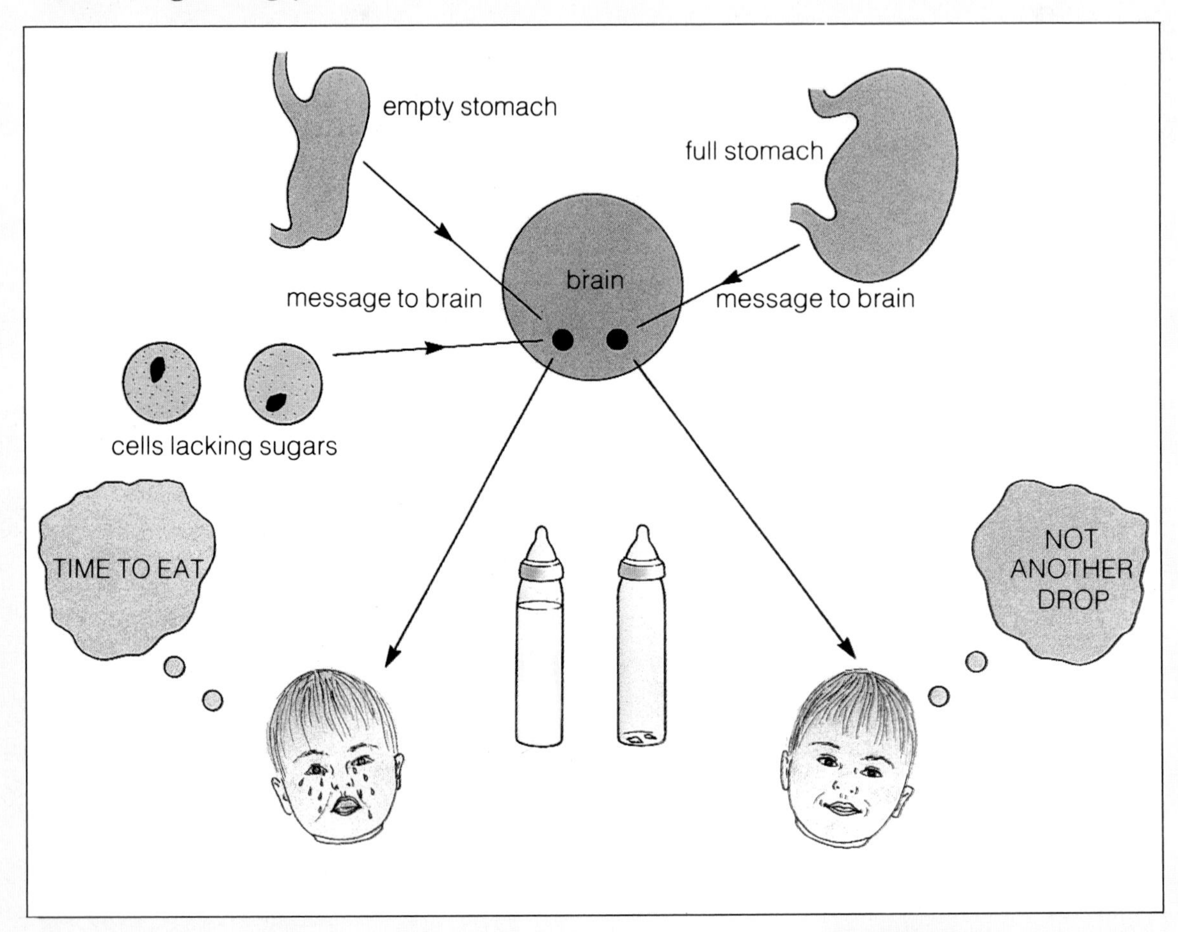

Early work on understanding digestion

William Beaumont was an American army surgeon. In 1823 he treated a man who had been shot in the stomach. The wound never healed properly. A small hole was left which opened into the stomach. For ten years, with the patient's agreement, he was able to remove samples of gastric juice from the stomach. He found out how different foods were broken down by the gastric juices. He also studied the movements of the stomach wall and discovered how the amounts of gastric juices varied during the day. As a result of his work a great deal was discovered about the roles of gastric juices in the digestion of food.

What do we know now?

There are many different enzymes in the body. Most of these are not concerned with digestion. The enzymes needed for digestion are produced in different regions of the alimentary canal and each one only breaks down a certain type of food.

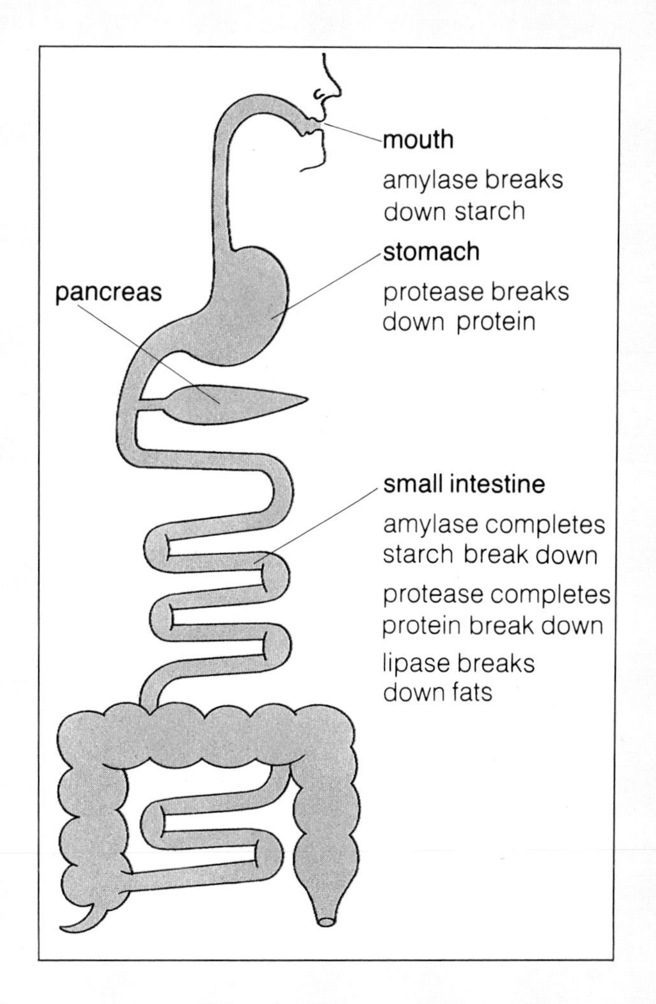

Phenylketonuria

About one in 8000 babies are born with this disease. An enzyme which is needed for the complete breakdown of proteins is not produced properly. As a result, **phenylalanine** and its breakdown product, **phenylketone**, collect in the blood. They are harmful and can cause brain damage.

This is a rare disease but it can be treated provided that it is detected when the baby is very young. A special diet is given with just the amount of protein needed for growth and no extra. Later the baby will be given a phenylalanine-free diet.

Coeliac disease

This is caused by a **sensitivity** to gluten, a mixture of proteins from wheat and rye. The disease leads to destruction of the villi in the small intestine which results in problems with food absorption.

A child suffering from this disease may be undernourished and stunted in growth. A gluten-free diet brings about remarkable improvements. Many baby foods now have no gluten added.

A *How often does a new-born baby need to be fed? Does breast-feeding or bottle-feeding make any difference to the frequency of feeding the baby?*

B *Imagine you were William Beaumont's patient who had been shot in the stomach. Write a brief description of how the experiment affected your life.*

C *Find out what job is done by the large intestine. Are there any enzymes in the large intestine?*

Questions and Activities

A Digestion breaks down large molecules in our food to smaller ones that we can use.

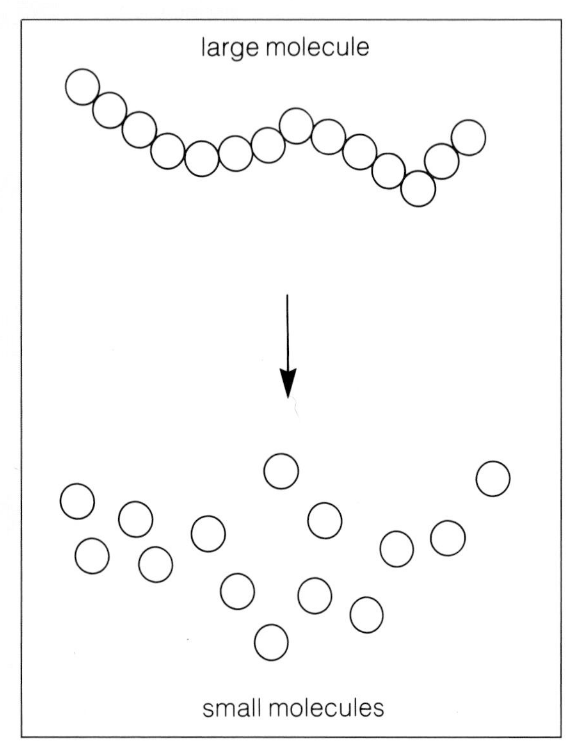

- What chemicals are produced by our body to help this breakdown?
- Why is digestion necessary?
- The small molecules are needed in all the cells of the body for growth and energy. Explain how they pass from the gut to the cells of the body.

B Mary suffers from phenylketonuria. It is the proteins in her diet which cause the problems. Why can she not be given a protein-free diet?

C Why does a child with coeliac disease appear thin, undernourished and undersized before treatment?

D This experiment was set up with egg white and some stomach juices.

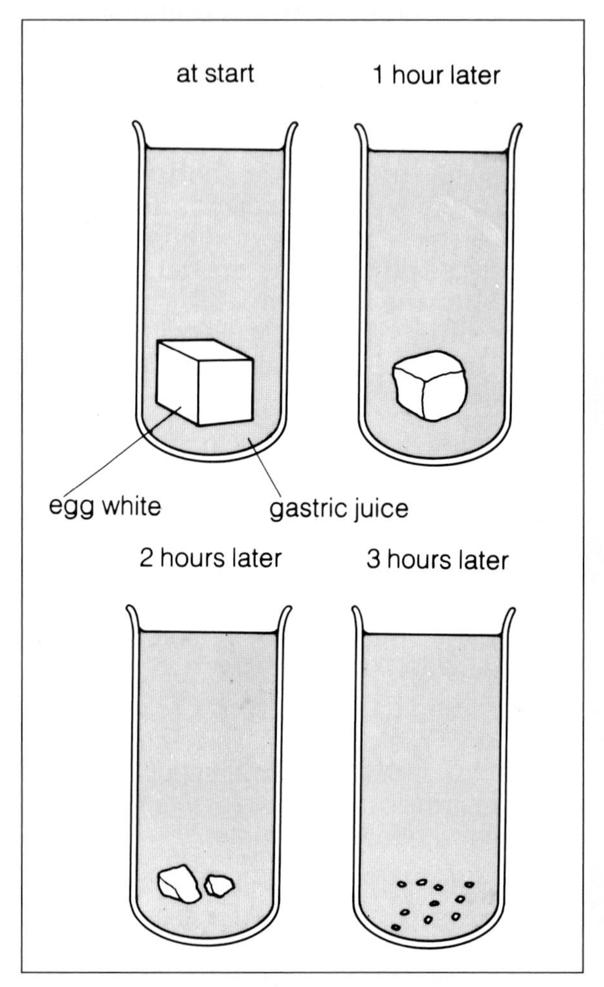

- What temperature would give the quickest results?
- What happens to the egg white?
- In a second experiment, the cube of egg white was broken up into small pieces. This time it disappeared after 1 hour. Explain why it broke down more quickly.
- What happens in our bodies to speed up the breakdown of a piece of egg white?

E An experiment was carried out to find which fluids from the alimentary canal would break down three different foods. Look back at the information on page 24 and then predict which foods would be changed. Copy out the chart and put a tick in the boxes where the fluid helps to digest the food.

type of food	saliva	gastric juice	intestinal fluids
meat			
butter			
bread			

F Sprinters often take glucose tablets just before the start of a race. Why is this of more use to them than a slice of bread?

G Look at the photograph of Maria on a drip (page 21). From what you have found out in this section, explain why the food is in solution.

H John has just recovered from a stomach ulcer. He has been advised to take care with his diet for the next few weeks as he still has problems digesting his food.

What types of food do you think would be the most suitable for him?

I Young mammals have an enzyme called rennin in their gastric juice which causes milk to clot.

Food must not pass too quickly along the small intestine or there will not be time for digestion to take place.

From these two pieces of information, explain why the enzyme **rennin** is especially important to young mammals.

J The enzyme **amylase** breaks down starch to sugars. It takes time to work and is affected by temperature. The activity of amylase is tested in an experiment.

Tube 1: starch suspension and amylase kept at 40°C
Tube 2: starch suspension and boiled amylase kept at 40°C
Tube 3: starch suspension and amylase kept at 20°C
Tube 4: starch suspension and amylase kept at 10°C

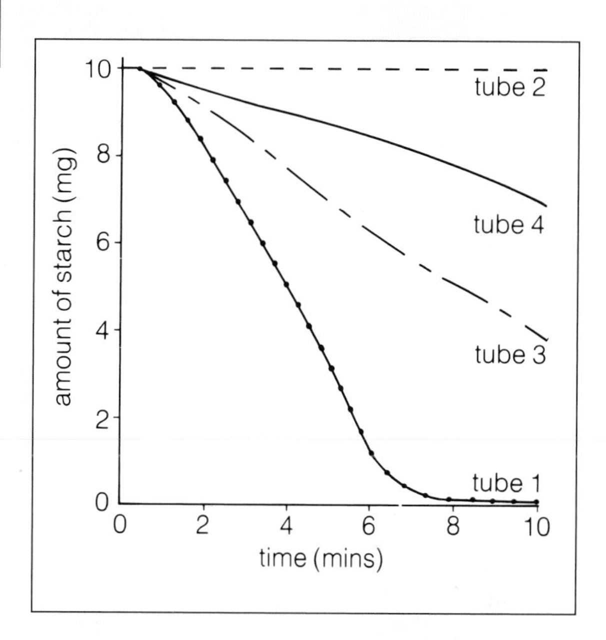

Study the graph showing the results of this experiment.

- What effect does boiling the enzyme have on its ability to break down starch?
- At which temperature does the enzyme work fastest?
- What do you think would happen to the rate of breakdown at 0°C?
- How long did it take for the enzyme to break down all the starch when kept at 40°C?

SURVIVAL

In 1984 Svetlana Savitskaya became the first woman to walk in space. This took place during the Salyut 7 space flight in July of that year.

A *The astronaut must take all her supplies with her. What will she need if she is going to spend several hours in space?*

B *Make a list of what you need from your surroundings to survive.*

C *Substances that our bodies do not need are passed back into our surroundings. What will the astronaut have to get rid of on her space walk?*

BREATH OF LIFE

The lungs are not like empty bags that take in air. They have a very complicated structure. The bronchi divide many times and end in millions of air-sacs. These are surrounded by tiny blood vessels.

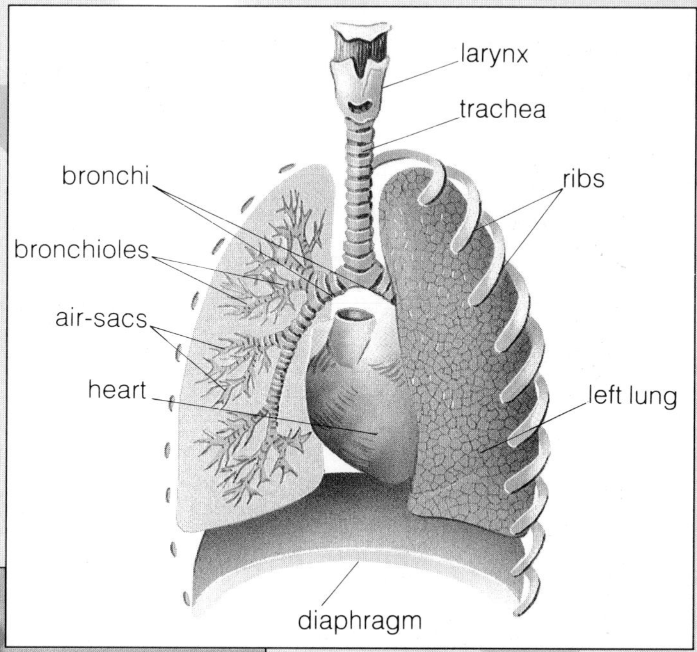

Diagram of the lungs

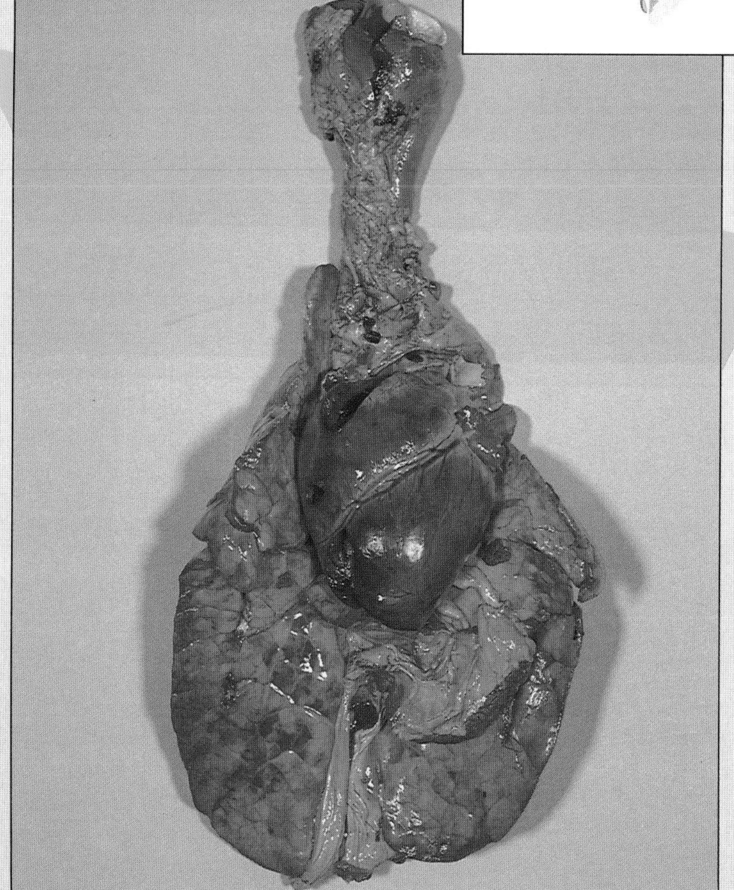

The lungs and heart of a sheep

A *Why do you think the lungs work better if they are made of millions of tiny air-sacs rather than a single large one?*

B *Why do the lungs need such a large number of blood vessels surrounding them?*

ENERGY FROM FOOD

WHICH GIVES THE MOST?

Fat gives the most energy for each gram than either protein or carbohydrate.

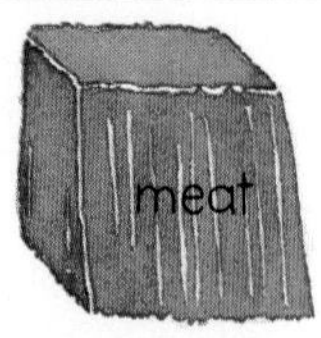

HOW MUCH ENERGY IS RELEASED FROM FOOD?

We can find out how much energy is stored in food by burning it and heating up water. The rise in temperature of the water gives a measure of how much energy was in the food.

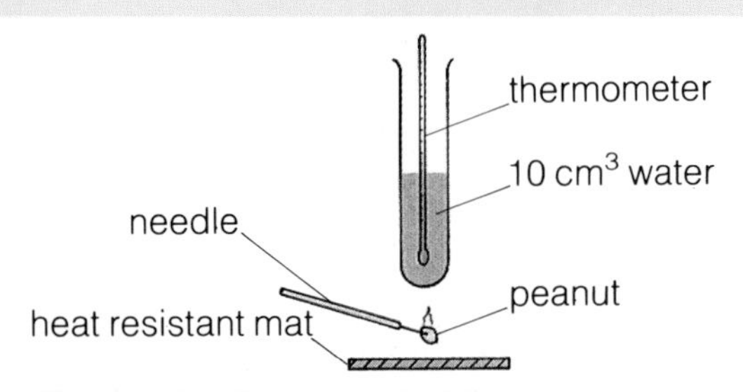

Peanut experiment

- *Measure the temperature of the water at the start.*
- *Weigh the peanut.*
- *Ignite the peanut.*
- *Let it burn under the tube of water.*
- *Measure the highest temperature of the water at the end.*
- *Weigh the remains of the peanut.*

This method can be used to measure the amount of heat energy produced when different foods are burnt. Remember that 4.2J will heat up 1 cm^3 of water by 1°C.

Food calorimeter

This method is used to obtain more accurate readings. The food is burnt in oxygen. The water is surrounded by an insulating layer to prevent heat loss. The food is set alight with electric ignition. The heat energy produced is measured in the same way as before.

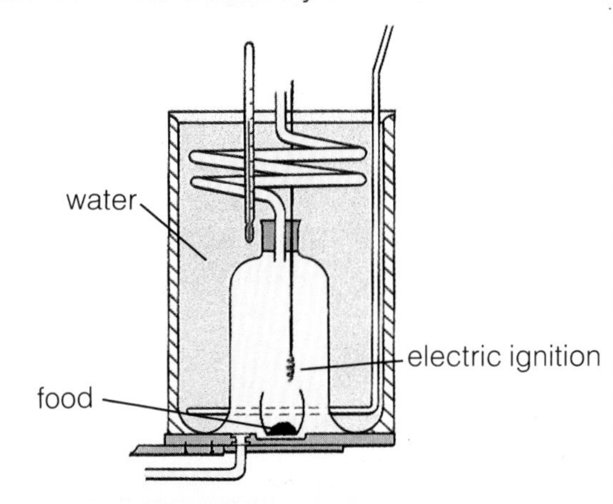

FOOD TO WATER AND CARBON DIOXIDE

white copper sulphate turning blue showing that burning food is producing water

limewater turning milky showing that carbon dioxide is being made

to pump

food burning

RESPIRATION

In all cells of the body, food is combined with oxygen to release energy. This process is called **respiration**.

Every cell in the body needs energy to work properly.

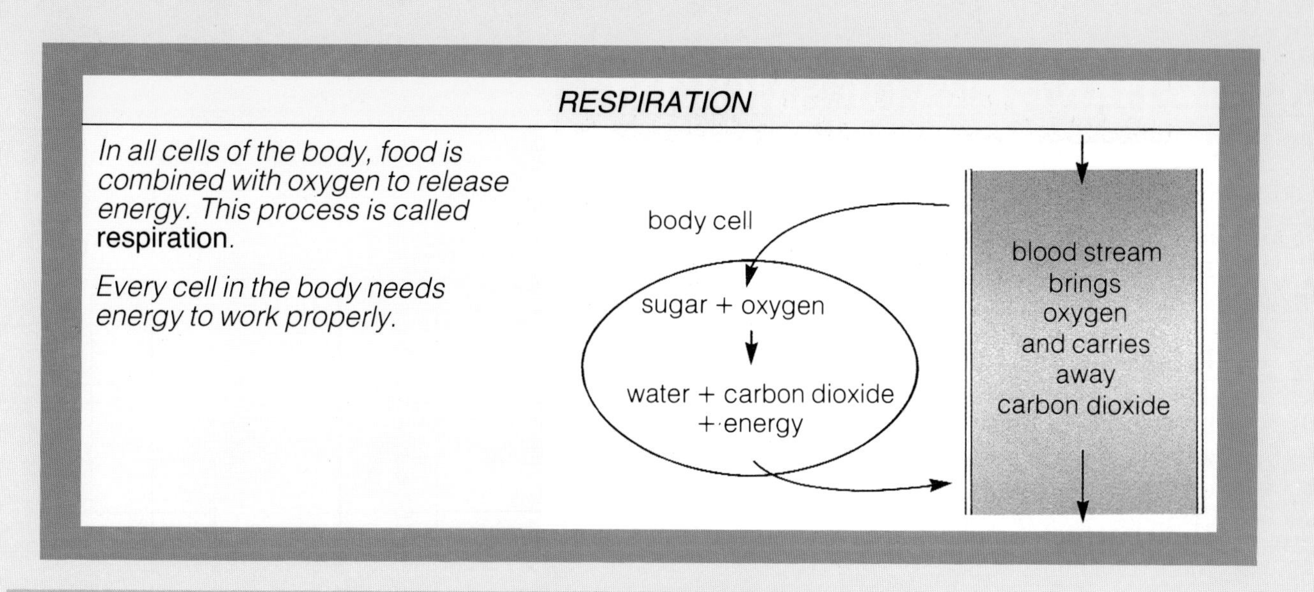

PASSAGE OF OXYGEN FROM THE AIR TO THE CELLS

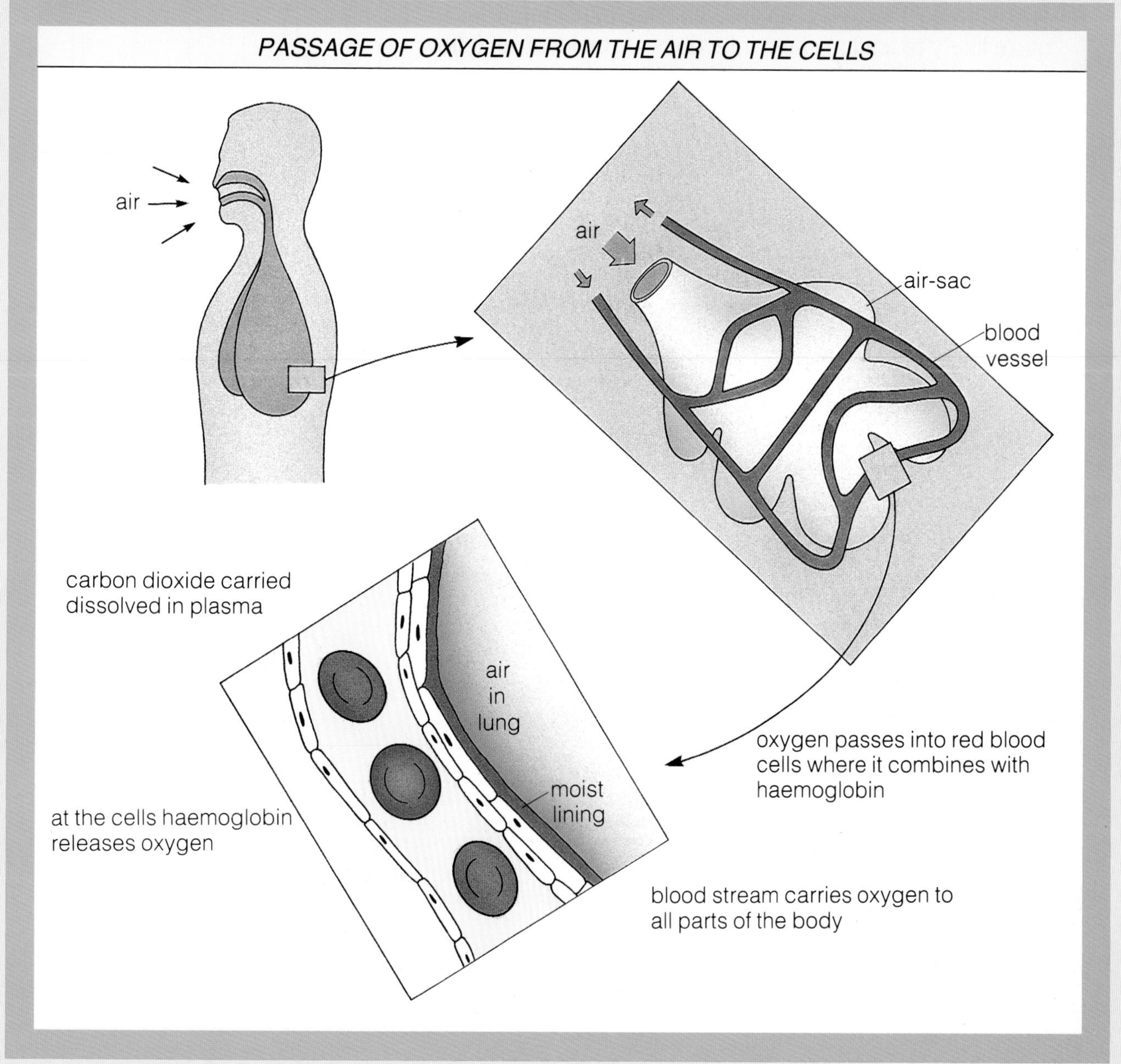

THE DANGERS OF SMOKING

If you smoke you are more likely to suffer from a serious illness than if you do not. Some diseases from which smokers suffer are listed below.

Lung cancer A tumour or growth develops in the lungs. The cells of the tumour increase in numbers and less of the lung is able to function. As this disease is usually in an advanced state before it is detected, treatment may not be effective.

Heart attack Smokers are two to three times more likely to die of a heart attack.

Bronchitis The extra mucus collecting in the lungs is more likely to lead to chest infections. Attacks often follow colds and gradually become more severe. The patient may become constantly breathless, be unable to walk properly and be unable to sleep unless propped up in a chair.

Emphysema The walls of the tiny air-spaces are broken down producing much larger air spaces. This reduces the surface area for oxygen absorption. More air has to be moved in and out of the lungs to give the same amount of oxygen and carbon dioxide. If the patient wishes to move about, the demand for oxygen becomes greater but the lungs cannot supply the muscles with sufficient oxygen. Breathing becomes more of a problem.

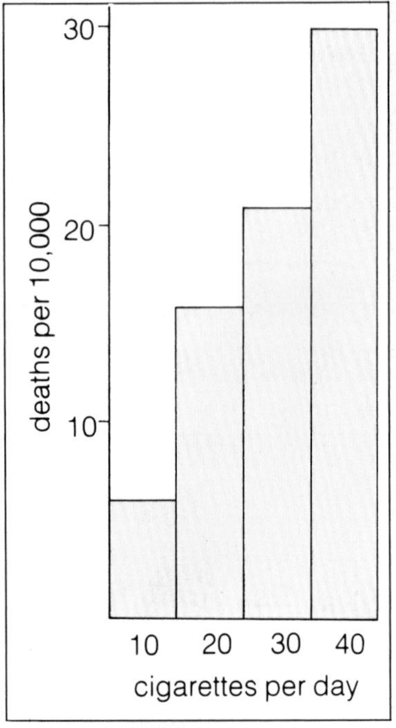

The more you smoke, the greater the risk

Into the lungs

Tar
- a heavy, brown sticky substance which collects in the lungs,
- causes more mucus or phlegm to be produced by the lungs,
- is known to contain chemicals which can cause cancer (carcinogens).

Nicotine
- passes from the air in the lungs into the blood stream,
- causes the heart to beat faster,
- increases the blood pressure,
- makes the blood clot more easily.

Carbon monoxide
- a poisonous gas, combines with haemoglobin in the red blood cells instead of oxygen,
- causes less oxygen to be taken to the cells for respiration.

- *You suffer from breathlessness*
- *You are less good at sport*
- *Your breath and clothes smell*
- *Your teeth and fingers become stained*

Smokers speak out

These people were interviewed to find out why they continued to smoke although they knew it was bad for their health.

Jenny Jones, age 35 who smokes 15–20 a day.
'I know smoking is bad for me. I used to be able to cycle five miles a day. Now I am out of breath by the time I get to the end of the road. I cough a lot too. I have tried to give up smoking but when I do, I just put on more weight.'

Harry Wood, age 62 who smokes 25 a day.
'I have been having terrible pains in my chest. I have to go to the hospital for tests. Maybe it's something to do with the smoking. I wish now I'd given up years ago. It's not worth bothering now.'

Cathy Lane, age 26 who smokes 30 a day.
'I'm three months pregnant. My doctor has told me I should give up smoking. He says it may harm the baby. I really want to but I find it very difficult.'

Suzy Cole, age 16 who smokes 10–12 a day.
'I'm young. It's all right if I smoke now. I will be able to give up when I'm older. Mind you, my friend doesn't like it much. She says it makes my breath smell but I don't notice it.'

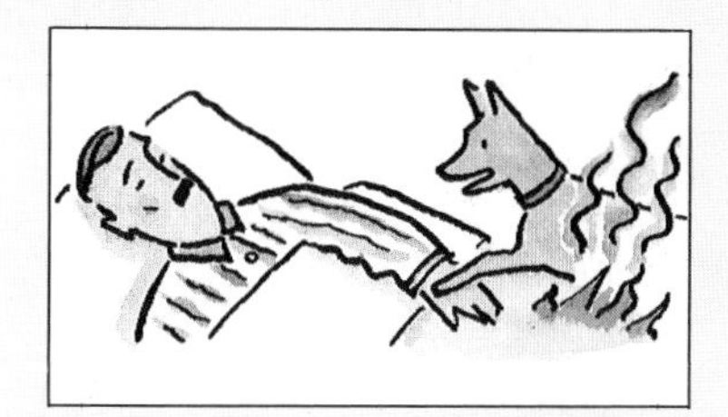

Gordon Lee, age 40 who smokes 30 a day.
'I was smoking in bed and fell asleep. The bed caught fire. If it wasn't for my dog I'd be dead. It's a pity about the house and furniture though.'

Jake Ladd, age 14 who never smokes.
'Everyone thinks I smoke because my clothes smell of cigarettes. It's my mum and dad who both smoke. I keep telling them to stop. I don't want them to get ill. I read that I could suffer from breathing in their fumes. I don't know if it's true.'

A *Make a list of all the disadvantages of smoking that you can find from these interviews.*

B *Discuss your findings in groups. Were your lists the same?*

C *Produce some interviews of your own for non-smokers. Find out from different people why they do not smoke or why they have given up.*

Questions and Activities

A Copy and complete these sentences using words from the list to help.

photosynthesis, respiration, oxygen, carbon dioxide, water, food, energy

All plants and animals carry out ____. Its main purpose is to produce ____ which can be used for movement, growth and warmth. ____ and ____ are needed and ____ ____ is produced as a waste product.

B Look at the chart below.

gas	percentage in inspired air	percentage in expired air
oxygen	20%	16%
nitrogen	78%	78%
carbon dioxide	0.04%	4%

(these figures are approximate)

- Why is there more oxygen in inspired air than expired air?
- Why is there more carbon dioxide in expired air than inspired air?
- The nitrogen percentage has not changed. Why not?
- What other changes would you expect if you compared inspired air with expired air?

C Non-smokers also suffer from lung diseases. These can be caused by:

- inhaling other people's cigarette smoke;
- sulphur dioxide in the air from burning fossil fuels;
- fumes from car exhausts;
- smogs in some cities;
- pollen causing hay fever.

Choose one of these and find out as much as you can about it.

D Look at the diagram of the lungs on page 29 and information in the **factfile**. Produce a flowchart to show the movement of oxygen from the air to the cells of the body for respiration. The stages have been given but they need sorting into their correct order.

- oxygen dissolves in moisture lining the air-sacs
- red blood cells carry oxygen to all cells
- air passes from the nose and into the trachea
- air passes from bronchioles into the air-sacs
- oxygen combines with haemoglobin in red blood cells
- oxygen diffuses from air-sacs into the blood stream
- trachea divides into two bronchi

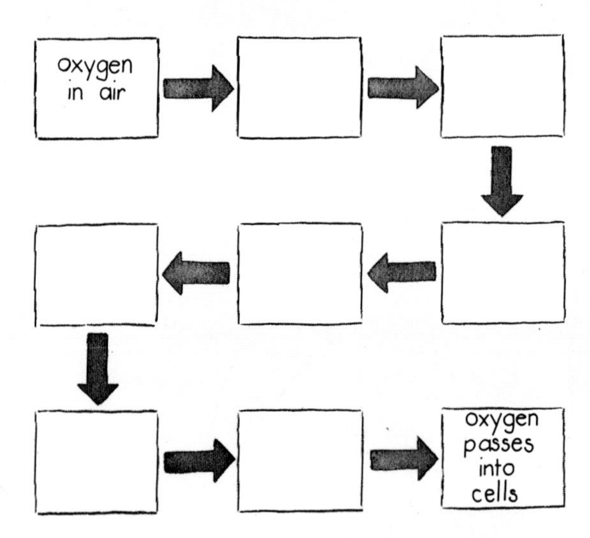

Your flowchart could look something like the one drawn but it will need to be larger.

E In the **factfile** you will find two different methods of measuring the amount of energy released from food. The peanut experiment does not give accurate results.

- Give as many reasons as you can for any errors.
- In what ways does the food calorimeter avoid these inaccuracies?

F Blood has many different functions. Some of them are listed below. For each one decide if red blood cells, white blood cells or plasma perform the function.

- carries dissolved carbon dioxide
- carries food in solution
- carries oxygen
- carries vitamins and mineral salts
- fights disease

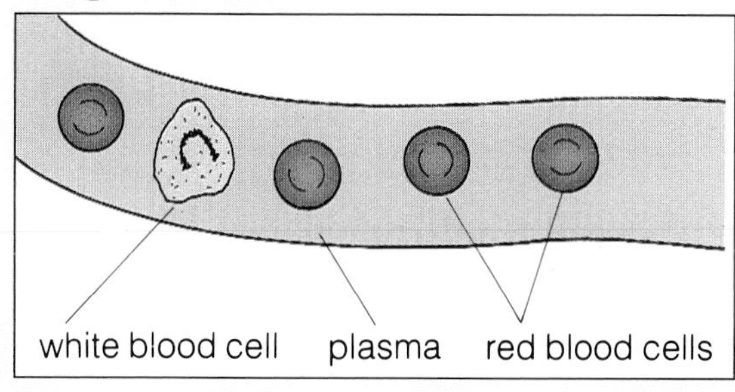

G This graph shows how the risk of getting lung cancer changes after giving up smoking.

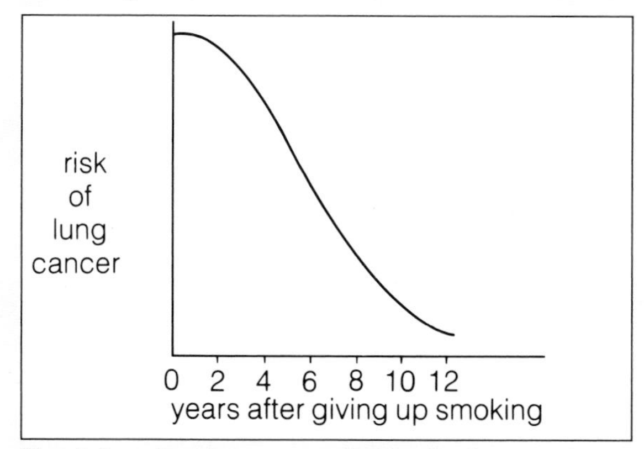

Explain why these results make it worthwhile giving up smoking.

H Look at the **factfile** to find out which food gives the most energy. With this information explain the reasons for the following statements about fat.

- Inuits (Eskimos) need more fat in their diet.
- Office workers need very little.
- People carrying out heavy manual work need more fat in their food.

I Find out which part of the cigarette causes the most harm? Give reasons for your answer. What advice would you give smokers about ways of making their habit less dangerous?

Now design your own anti-smoking poster or badge.

J Jo's mother has just discovered that Jo has been smoking cigarettes. She is very angry as she has always made Jo fully aware of the dangers of smoking.

Jo's father is concerned. He does smoke himself but has always made it clear that he doesn't want Jo smoking.

- In groups of three, choose one person to be Jo's mother, one to be Jo's father and one as Jo. Each person should try to make their views on smoking clear to the others.
- Compare your play with a second group. Did you reach any conclusions about who is right and wrong?

HARD WORK

When you take exercise changes happen in your body to help you to work harder. One of the first things that you will notice is that you will start to sweat.

A *Think of the ways you have noticed your own body adjusting when you work hard. Put them into a table. Try to think of a reason for each one.*

change when exercising	advantage of change
sweating	gets rid of extra heat

B *After an athlete has recovered from a race he will probably feel hungry. Explain why this happens.*

FIT TO DROP

Being fit helps us to do better at sports, but fitness is not just for athletes. We all need to be as fit as we can.

A Think about the exercise you take. Is your diet a healthy one? Are you making any of the mistakes shown in the cartoon? Write down just two changes you could make to be more fit.

B Brainstorm all of the advantages of being fit. Then make a list of them, putting them in the order which is most important to you.

FACTFILE

WORKING HARD AND KEEPING FIT

CHANGES DURING EXERCISE

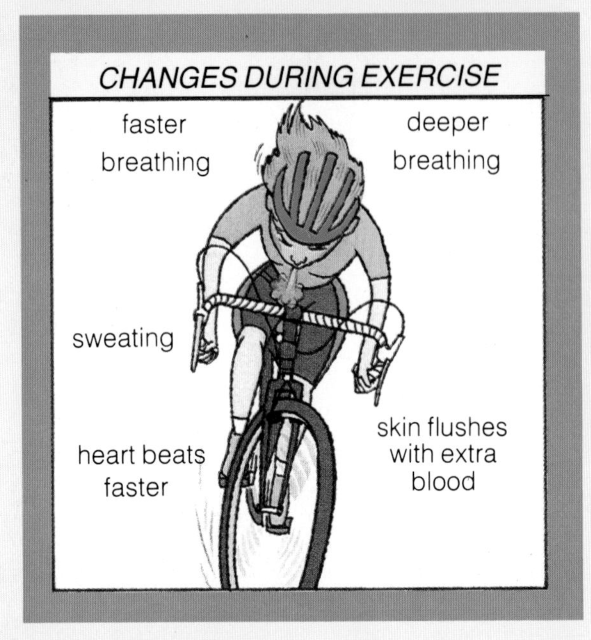

WORKING HARD USES MORE ENERGY

When we exercise the respiration reaction is boosted to give more energy to the muscles. The muscles use more food and oxygen and produce more carbon dioxide, water and energy.

food + oxygen → carbon dioxide + water + energy

- *More digested food is delivered to the muscles.*
- *More oxygen is taken from the lungs to the muscles.*
- *More waste carbon dioxide has to be taken back to the lungs to be breathed out.*
- *Waste heat needs to be lost through the skin.*

THE HEART PUMPS FASTER DURING EXERCISE

When the heart beats faster things can be carried to and from the muscles more quickly. Everything is carried in the blood.

- *Larger amounts of digested food can be supplied to the muscles.*
- *More oxygen can be carried to the muscles from the lungs.*
- *Waste carbon dioxide can be taken to the lungs more quickly.*
- *Waste heat can be sent to the skin to be lost.*

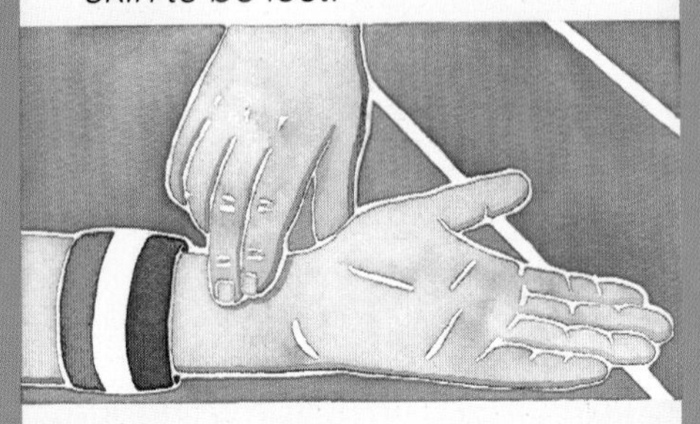

Average pulse rate at rest = 75 beats/min
During exercise = 100 beats/min

BREATHING AND EXERCISE

We breathe deeper and faster during exercise. This lets us take in the extra oxygen we need, and gets rid of carbon dioxide more quickly.

	before exercise	during exercise
respiration rate (breaths per minute)	15	22
tidal volume (litres per breath)	0.5	3.0
lung output (litres per minute)	7.5	66

Altogether we can increase the amount of air going through our lungs in a minute by nine or ten times.

A marathon runner uses energy at ten times the normal rate

KEEPING COOL

We could easily become dangerously hot because of the waste heat we make. Our bodies have three ways of keeping our temperature down to 37°C.

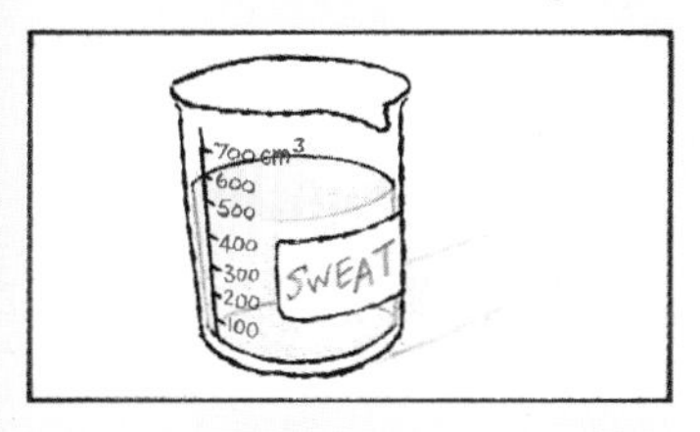

Evaporating sweat
When sweat evaporates, it takes heat from our skin. In one hour of gymnastics we could loose half a litre of sweat. No wonder it makes us thirsty!

Convection: hot air rises
The air near our hot skin gets warm. The hot air rises up and carries the heat away with it. This is called a convection current.

The skin is a radiator
Extra blood flowing in the skin makes us look more red. It brings heat to the surface. You can feel the heat shining or **radiating** *from a hot person.*

KEEP FIT

Fitness is all about the state of the heart, blood vessels and lungs. In a fit person they adjust easily to exercise.

The heart *like any other muscle grows larger and stronger with exercise. A fit heart beats slowly when supplying resting muscles with blood. It can easily cope with the need for more blood during exercise, and soon goes back to normal afterwards.*

Blood vessels *need to be clear of blockages to let the blood run through them quickly.*

Fit lungs *are large and have a good blood supply so they can put oxygen into the blood easily. Fit lungs would never be blocked up with tar from cigarettes!*

Overeating *is particularly bad for your fitness. Just carrying the extra weight is a handicap. The heart and blood vessels may also be damaged.*

Aerobic exercises *improve the condition of your heart and lungs.*

Swimming

Cycling

Jogging

CORONARY HEART DISEASE

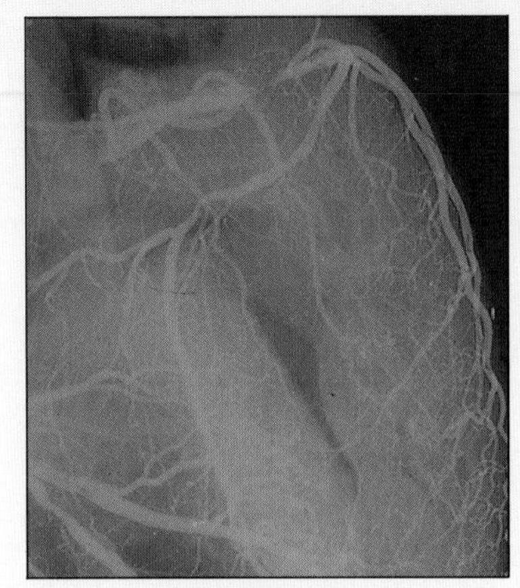
The coronary arteries

Britain is one of the worst countries in the world for heart disease. It causes over a quarter of all deaths which adds up to about 400 every day.

The heart is a muscle, and to keep working it needs food and oxygen. It has its own special blood supply, brought to it in the **coronary arteries**. They can become 'furred-up' by something called **cholesterol**. This is a fatty substance which builds up if we eat too much fat.

Eventually a piece of cholesterol may break loose, or a blood clot may fill up the passage. No blood can reach the heart muscle. It goes short of oxygen, and may stop. The victim has suffered a heart attack.

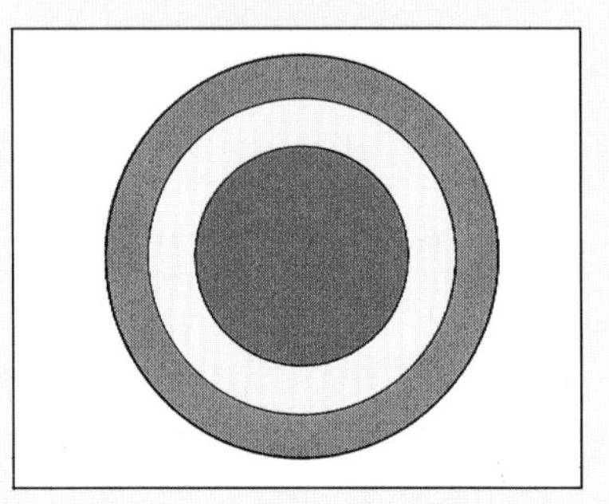
A healthy artery has smooth sides and a wide channel for the blood

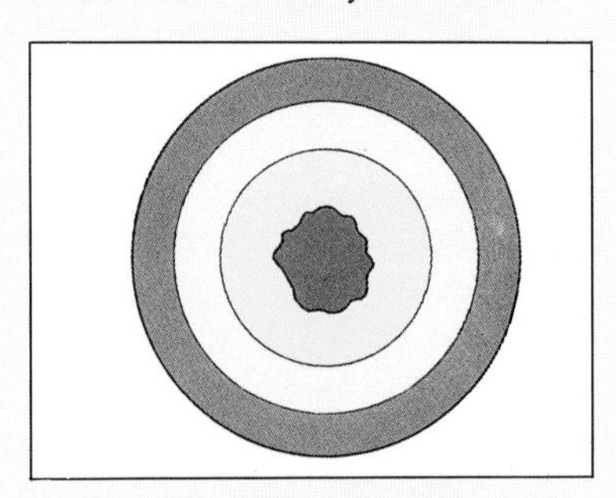
A diseased artery contains cholesterol which makes the walls rough and narrows the channel

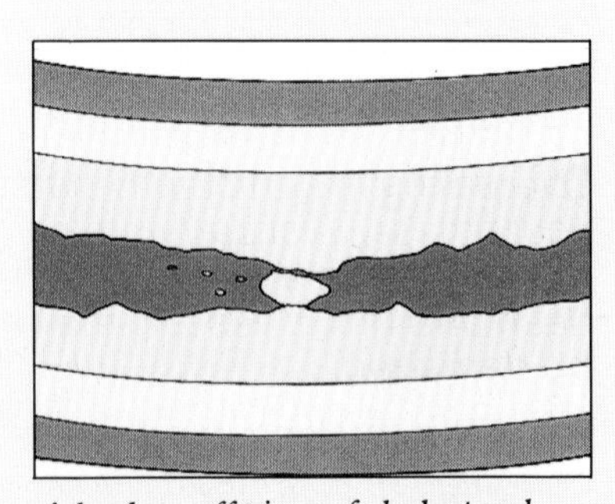
A broken off piece of cholesterol has stopped blood flowing. A blood clot can do the same thing

Avoiding heart disease

- Cut down on fried foods.
- Avoid saturated fats in meat, butter, cream. Eat unsaturated fats from fish and vegetable oils.
- Do not smoke.
- Take plenty of exercise.

A *Look at packets of all sorts of butters, margarines, cooking fats and oils.*

Sort them into two lists:

- *saturated fats;*
- *unsaturated fats.*

B *Write a note to a parent explaining which brands of oils and fats are the healthiest to use at home.*

HOW DO YOU MEASURE UP?

Getting fit means working on three main things – stamina, suppleness and strength. Different exercises build up these parts of fitness.

fitness	body need	exercise
stamina	a strong and healthy heart	aerobic exercises – cycling, jogging, swimming
suppleness	flexible joints	stretching exercises – dancing, gymnastics, yoga and swimming
strength	strong muscles	pulling and lifting – rowing, weight lifting, swimming

The most important from the point of view of health is to make sure the heart is strong.

Aerobic exercises are ones which make you breathe hard and put up your pulse, but not to the maximum. They need to be done two or three times a week to do any good, and each session should last 20 minutes.

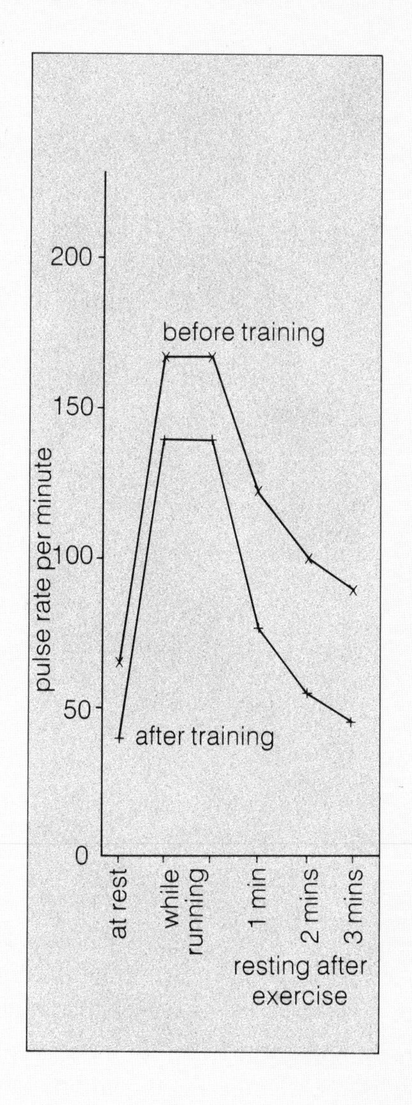

Measuring fitness

We can see how fit a person is from their heart rate. When a person is fit their heart beats more slowly, and it goes back to normal quickly after exercise.

This graph shows the changes in a man who got fit by regular jogging. Notice that once he was fit his heart rate was more or less back to normal after only three minutes rest.

How fit are the people in your class? Try these two tests of fitness. Are the people who come out best the same ones who do most sport?

A Record the resting pulse rate
Get everyone to sit quietly for five minutes. Then everyone should take their neighbour's pulse while they keep on sitting still. Put all the results in order in a table, starting with the slowest.

B Return to normal after exercise
Decide on a simple exercise that can be done in the classroom. Get everyone to do exactly the same amount – this has got to be a fair test. Afterwards everyone should take their pulse every minute until it is back to normal. Record how long it takes each person to go back to their resting pulse rate. Put these results in order of fitness, with the fastest recoverers at the top.

Questions and Activities

A The body can make many changes to help it work hard. Make a summary of them. Do it by filling in this chart.

Breathing is deeper and more . . .	More oxygen is put into the blood. More ____ is removed.
The heart beats faster.	Blood is supplied to the ____ and ____ more quickly.
Sweating increases.	Waste heat can be lost when the sweat . . .
We wear fewer clothes . . .	Convection currents of warm air carry away . . .
Blood vessels in the skin . . .	Extra radiation cools us down.

B Coronary heart disease is caused by eating too much saturated fat. Lack of exercise and smoking add to the problem.

Think about your own life. Write down some changes you could make to stop yourself getting heart disease when you are older.

C Here is the word equation for respiration.

food + **oxygen** → **energy** + **water** + **carbon dioxide**

- Use the equation to explain why your muscles need to be supplied with more blood when you run.
- What waste products have to be got rid of after exercise?

D Use the information in the **factfile** about losing heat to explain the following statements.

- We feel very hot if we take exercise wearing clothes made of artificial fibres like nylon instead of porous cotton.
- The wind seems to be colder when we come out of the sea than it was before we went in.
- Alcohol makes the blood vessels in our skin widen artificially, so the skin feels warmer, but it is dangerous to give a person who has got very cold a drink of brandy *to warm them up*.

Don't risk it!

E Make a poster which could be used to warn people of the risks of coronary heart disease.

In a poster you cannot cover everything. Decide on the main points you wish to get over before you begin.

Careful dad!

Angela's dad has decided to take part in the Bedton fun run. He is collecting sponsors to buy Angela's school some science books.

Angela is a bit worried about this. The only exercise he gets normally is when he walks round to the corner shop for his cigarettes. Even that makes him out of puff, and it takes him five minutes to get his breath back afterwards.

He is also overweight, as he loves to eat large meals.

There are six months to go before the run. Just enough time to get him ready!

Angela realises she has three main jobs to do. She must convince her dad that he is in no fit state to run at the moment. Then she needs to explain to him what he has to do to get fit. Last of all she will need a way of measuring how his fitness improves over the next few months.

- Finish this note which Angela writes to make her dad see that he's got some preparation to do.

Dear Dad
It's really nice of you to do the run for our new books, but I don't think you are quite ready for it at the moment...

- Make a list of the changes he is going to have to make if he is to be ready for the run.
- How could Angela measure her father's improving fitness? Look back to page 41 for a clue.

DATAPAGES

Food values

The tables refer to 100g of each food.

	food	energy (kJ)	fat (g)	carbohydrate (g)	water (g)	protein (g)	calcium (mg)	iron (mg)	vitamin A (µg)	vitamin B1 (mg)	vitamin B2 (mg)	vitamin C (mg)	vitamin D (µg)	fibre (g)
MEAT, FISH AND POULTRY	bacon, fried	2090	45	0	27	23	0	1.2	0	0.4	0.2	0		
	ham	500	5	0	73	18		1.2	0	0	0.3	0		
	hamburgers, fried	1090	17	7	53	20	35	3.1	0	0	0.2	0		
	pork, roast leg	1210	20	0	52	27	0	1.3	0	0.7	0.3	0		
	sausage roll	2090	36	33	23	7	70	1.3	120	0.1	0.04	0		
	sausage, pork	1340	25	11	45	14	60	1.5	0	0	0.2	0		
	beef, corned	920	12	0	59	27	0	3.0	0	0	0.2	0		
	beef, fried steak	1050	15	0	56	29	0	3.2	0	0.08	0.35	0		
	beef, roast sirloin	1170	21	0	54	24	0	2.0	0	0.06	0.25	0		
	beef, stewed steak	920	11	0	57	30	0	3.0	0	0.03	0.33	0		
	lamb, roast leg	1130	18	0	55	26	0	2.5	0	0.12	0.30	0		
	chicken, roast	630	5	0	68	25	0	0.8	0	0.1	0.2	0		
	cod, fried in batter	840	10	8	61	20	80	0.5	0	0.1	0.1	0		
	fish fingers	960	13	17	56	13.5	45	0.7	45	0.1	0.1	0		
	mackerel	920	16	0	64	19	25	1.0	45	0.1	0.35	0	17.5	
	plaice, fried	960	14	9	60	18	70	0.8	0	0.2	0.2	0		
CEREALS	bran, wheat	840	5.5	27	8	14	10	13	0	1	0.4	0		44
	bread, brown	920	2.2	45	39	9	100	2.5	0	0.25	0.05	0		5
	bread, white	960	1.7	50	39	7.8	100	1.7	0	0.2	0.03	0		4
	bread, wholemeal	920	2.7	42	40	8.8	25	2.5	0	0.3	0.08	0		9
	chapatis	840	1	44	46	7.0	60	2.0	0	0.23	0.04	0		4
	rice, boiled white	500	0.3	30	70	2.0	0	0	0	0	0	0		3
	pasta, spaghetti	500	0.3	26	72	4.0	0	0.4	0	0	0	0		2
	All-bran	1040	2.5	46	5	13	85	9	0	1	1.5	0	27	
	cornflakes	1500	0.5	82	3	8.0	0	7	0	1	1.5	0	11	
	oatmeal porridge	190	1	8	90	1.5	0	0.5	0	0.05	0	0		1
	Shredded Wheat	1340	3	68	7.5	10.5	40	4	0	0.3	0.05	0		11
	Weetabix	1420	3.5	70	3.8	11.5	30	7.6	0	1	1.5	0		9
SWEETS	biscuits, plain	1970	20	66	4.5	10	110	2.0	0	0.15	0.1	0		
	biscuits, chocolate	2050	24	66	2.5	7	85	2.0	0	0.1	0.1	0		
	cake, fruit	1380	11	58	20	4	75	1.8	120	0.1	0.1	0	1.1	3
	chocolate, milk	2220	30	59	2	8	220	1.6	0	0.1	0.2	0		
	honey	1210	0	76	23	0	0	0.4	0	0	0	0		
	ice cream	710	7	25	64	4	140	0.2	0	0.04	0.2	0		
	jam	1090	0	69	30	0	0	1.5	0	0	0	10		
	marmalade	1090	0	69	28	0	35	0.6	50	0	0	10		
	Mars bar	1840	19	67	7	5	160	1	0	0.05	0.2	0		
	sugar	1630	0	100	0	0	0	0	0	0	0	0		
DRINKS	beer	130	0	2	–	0	0	0	0	0	0	0		
	fruit juice	170	0	10	87	0	0	0.3	0	0.04	0	25		
	lemonade	80	0	6	95	0	0	0	0	0	0	0		
	spirits, e.g. whisky	920	0	0	–	0	0	0	0	0	0	0		
	wine, red	290	0	0	–	0	0	1	0	0	0	0		

The tables for fibre and vitamin D only show good sources. We can also make our own vitamin D in our skin when the sun shines on it.

	food	energy (kJ)	fat (g)	carbohydrate (g)	water (g)	protein (g)	calcium (mg)	iron (mg)	vitamin A (µg)	vitamin B1 (mg)	vitamin B2 (mg)	vitamin C (mg)	vitamin D (µg)	fibre (g)
	apples	150	0	9	65	0.2	0	0.2	0	0.03	0	2		2
	bananas	330	0.3	20	70	1	0	0.4	200	0.04	0.07	10		3
	bean sprouts	40	0	0.8	95	1.6	0	1.0	0	0	0.03	0		3
	beans, baked	270	0.5	10	74	5	45	1.4	0	0.07	0.05	0		
	beans, broad	210	0.6	7	84	4	20	1	40	0.1	0.04	15		4
	beans, mung (dahl)	420	4	11	73	6	35	2.6	0	0.1	0.04	0		4
	beans, runner	85	0.2	3	91	2	25	0.7	60	0.03	0.07	5		
	blackberries	120	0	6	80	1.5	60	1	15	0.03	0.04	20		
	brussel sprouts	80	0	1.7	92	3	25	0.5	60	0.06	0.1	40		3
	cabbage	60	0	2.3	93	1.7	40	0.4	50	0.03	0.03	20		2
	carrots, boiled	80	0	4	92	0.6	40	0.4	12000	0.05	0.04	4		3
	cauliflower, boiled	40	0	0.8	95	1.5	0	0.4	5	0.06	0.06	20		2
	celery, raw	40	0	1.3	94	1	50	0.6	0	0.03	0.03	7		2
	cucumber	40	0	2	96	0.6	25	0.3	0	0.04	0.04	8		0.5
	grapefruit	80	0	5	90	0.5	0	0.3	0	0.05	0	40		0.5
	grapes, white	250	0	15	75	0.6	20	0.3	0	0.04	0	0		0.5
FRUIT AND	lettuce	40	0	1	96	1	25	0.9	200	0.07	0.08	15		1.5
VEGETABLES	melons	100	0	5	93	0.5	0	0.5	1000	0.05	0.03	25		1
	mushrooms	60	0.6	0	92	2	0	1	0	0.1	0.4	3		3
	onions, spring	150	0	8.5	87	1	140	1.2	0	0.03	0.05	25		3
	oranges	150	0	9	85	1	40	0.3	50	0.1	0.03	50		2
	peanuts	2390	50	9	4	24	60	2	0	1	0.1	0		8
	peas	290	0.4	11	78	6	0	2	50	0.3	0.2	25		5
	peppers	60	0.4	2	94	1	0	0.04	40	0	0.03	100		1
	plums	80	0	6	77	0.5	0	0.03	30	0.05	0.03	0		2
	potatoes, baked	360	0	20	58	2	0	0.06	0	0.1	0.03	10		2
	potato chips	1050	11	37	47	4	0	0.9	0	0.1	0.04	10		
	rhubarb	20	0	1	94	0.5	100	0.4	0	0	0.03	10		2
	spinach	130	0.5	1.5	85	5	600	4	1000	0.1	0.15	25		6
	strawberries	100	0	6	88	0.5	20	0.7	5	0	0.03	60		2
	sweet potatoes	360	0.6	20	72	1	0	0.6	700	0.1	0.05	15		2
	sweetcorn	330	0.5	16	73	3	0	0.6	40	0.05	0.08	5		4
	tomatoes, raw	60	0	3	93	1	0	0.4	15	0.1	0.05	20		1.5
	tomato soup	250	3	6	84	1	0	0.4	60	0	0	0		
	yam, boiled	500	0	30	66	1.5	0	0.3	0	0.05	0	2		4
	butter	3140	82	0	15.4	0.5	15	0.2	1000	0	0	0	0.8	
	cheese, cheddar	1670	34	0	37	26	800	0.4	400	0.04	0.5	0	0.3	
	cheese, cottage	420	0.5	1.5	79	14	60	0.1	30	0	0.2	0		
	cream	840	21.9	3	72	2.4	80	0.3	250	0.3	0.1	0	0.2	
DAIRY	eggs, raw	630	10.9	0	74.8	12.3	50	2	140	0.1	0.5	0	1.8	
PRODUCE	eggs, scrambled	1050	23	0	62	10	60	2	150	0.1	0.3	0	8.0	
	margarine	3060	81	0	16	0	0	0	1000	0	0	0		
	milk	270	3.8	4.7	87.6	3.3	120	0	50	0.05	0.2	1	0.03	
	oil, vegetable	3770	100	0	0	0	0	0	0	0	0	0		
	yoghurt	210	1	6	86	5	180	0	0	0.05	0.3	0		

Extension Activities

How much should I eat?

You can use the tables of food values on the previous pages to decide what food you should eat.

This table shows the amount of each that you need in one day.

	energy (kJ)	protein (g)	calcium (mg)	iron (mg)	vitamin A (µg)	vitamin B1 (mg)	vitamin B2 (mg)	vitamin C (mg)
boys, 15-17 years	12,000	72	600	12	750	1.2	1.7	30
men, 18–34 years, moderately active	12,000	72	500	10	750	1.2	1.6	30
girls, 15–17 years	9,000	53	600	12	750	0.9	1.7	30
women, 18–34 years, most occupations	9,500	54	500	12	750	0.9	1.3	30

- The recommended daily amount for vitamin D varies. In the summer you may not need to eat any at all, as you can make all you need in your skin.

  People who stay indoors all the time may need 10µg each day.
- You can make up the energy from foods with fat or carbohydrate. It is more healthy to choose carbohydrates. Just include small amounts of fat.
- Try to include foods with plenty of fibre in your diet.

SYMBOLS AND UNITS

symbol	unit
J	*joule*
kJ	*kilojoule*
g	*gram*
mg	*milligram*
µg	*microgram*

1kJ = 1,000 J
1g = 1,000 mg
1g = 1,000,000 µg

SIZE OF PORTIONS

These figures are for normal servings. You can use them to estimate how much portions of other things weigh. To get a better idea you could weigh things at home on the kitchen scales.

Cod fillet	170g
Roast beef	140g
Cornflakes	30g
Slice of bread	30g
Teaspoon of sugar	6g
Glass of any drink	200g
Chips or potatoes	150g
Sprouts (or other vegetables)	110g
Apple	120g
Cheese (in a sandwich)	15g
Butter (in one slice of bread)	5g
Egg	70g

It all adds up

Now you can work out how good your diet is. Say you had a boiled egg, two slices of bread and butter, an apple and a glass of fruit juice. The table shows you how to work out what the meal contains.

food	portion (g)	energy (kJ)	fat (g)	carbohydrate (g)	protein (g)	calcium (mg)	iron (mg)	vitamin A (μg)	vitamin B1 (mg)	vitamin B2 (mg)	vitamin C (mg)	vitamin D (μg)	fibre (g)
1 egg	70	441	7.6	0	8.6	35	1.4	98	0.07	0.35	0	1.26	
2 slices wholemeal bread	60	552	1.6	25.2	5.3	15	1.5	0	0.18	0.05	0		5.4
butter	10	314	8.2	0	0.05	1.5	0.02	100	0	0	0	0.08	
1 apple	120	180	0	10.8	0.24	0	0.24	0	0.04	0	2.4		2.4
1 glass of juice	200	340	0	20	0	0	0.6	0	0.08	0	50		
Totals	460	1824	17.4	56	14.19	51.5	3.76	198	0.57	0.4	52.4	1.34	7.8

A John is a builder. This is what he has for lunch.

sausages	150g
chips	200g
beer (2 pints)	1000g

Work out what his dinner contains, setting it out in the same way as the table above.

- What do you think of his meal?
- What is good about it?
- Has it got too much of anything?
- Has it got too little of anything?
- How could his meal be improved?

B Write down what you had for your main meal yesterday. Use a chart to work out what it contained.

Use this formula to work out how much of your daily needs your meal gave you.

$$\frac{\text{amount in meal}}{\text{daily requirement}} \times 100\%$$

If you are a girl and your meal contained 3000kJ of energy then:

$$\frac{3000}{9000} \times 100\% = 33.3\%$$

The meal gave you 33.3% of your daily energy.

Do similar sums for energy, protein and vitamin C.

C Plan a whole day's meals for yourself. Make sure they contain everything you need.

Index

Aerobic exercise 41
Air 31
Amylase 23, 25
Anorexia 9
Anus 20
Artery, diseased 40
Artery, healthy 40
Attitudes to smoking 33
Avoiding heart disease 40

Balanced diet 12
Balanced meals 12, 15
Blood clots 40
Blood plasma 23
Blood pressure 32
Blood stream 31
Blood vessels 22, 23
Body temperature 5, 6
Breathing 38
Bronchi 29
Bronchitis 32

Cancer 32
Captain Scott 16
Calorimeter 30
Carbohydrates 14, 15
Carbon dioxide 31
Carcinogens 32
Carotene 17
Changes in appetite 8
Cholesterol 40
Coeliac disease 25
Collagen 15
Copper sulphate 30
Coronary heart disease 40

Daily energy requirements 7
Danger of smoking 32
Diet 46, 47
Diet plans 46, 47
Deficiency diseases 15
Digestion 20, 22

E numbers 17
Effects of smoking 32
Emphysema 32
Energy for warmth 6
Energy loss 5
Energy to grow 6
Energy to move 6
Enzymes 22, 23, 25
Exercise 37, 38, 39, 41
Exercising the heart 38, 39, 41

Fat 14, 15
Fibre 14, 15
Fitness 36, 37, 38, 39, 41
Food additives 17
Food energy 4, 5, 6, 7, 30
Food values table 44, 45

Gastric juices 24, 25
Gluten-free diet 25

Haemoglobin 31
Healthy weight 7, 8, 9
Heart attack 40
Heart rate 39, 41
Heat radiation 5
Human energy needs 4, 5, 6, 7
Hypothermia 7, 11

Joule 6, 7

Large intestine 20, 22, 23, 25
Limewater 30
Lipase 25
Liver 20
Lung cancer 32
Lungs 29, 31

Malnutrition 9, 13
Measuring energy 6
Minerals 14, 15
Mouth 20, 25
Mucus 32

Oils 14

Pancreas 25
Peanut experiment 30
Phenylketonuria 25
Phlegm 32
Plasma 23, 31
Protease 25
Protein 14, 15, 19

Red blood cells 23, 31
Respiration 30, 31

Scurvy 16
Small intestine 20, 22, 23, 25
Stamina 41
Starch 23
Stomach 20, 22, 24, 25
Strength 41
Sugar 24, 30, 31
Survival 28
Sweating 39

Tidal volume 38

Undernourishment 25

Villi 23, 25
Visking tubing 23
Vitamin C 16
Vitamins 14, 15, 46

Water 14
White blood cells 23
William Beaumont 24